To

int

Mong chisholm

The HindSight Project

J. McKay

– Third Voice Publishing –

First published by Third Voice Publishing in 2021

Publishing services provided by Lumphanan Press
www.lumphananpress.co.uk

Cover: original painting by Glenda Waterworth
www.glendawaterworth.com

ISBN: 978-1-5272-9429-5

Printed by Imprint Digital, UK

'Women are used to bearing burdens and taking blame'
Barbara Pym, Crampton Hodnet

Contents

Prologue

I'm in an Italian restaurant in Dumfries, currently rated the best in town, savouring a particularly good risotto. I am looking forward to a relaxed, enjoyable evening, encouraged by the warm ambience. Across the table is Iain, the latest of the transient relationships I've had since my divorce eight years ago. All the men have been in their sixties like myself, living on their own, embracing the modern concept of friends with benefits. Unfortunately, the benefits tend to diminish with time as unreliable erections and drying vaginas take their toll.

Iain has spoilt my enjoyment and I want to leave. He has recounted an incident from some years ago, while working on Canna with a team of archaeologists. It holds my interest, but then he begins a related story that I've heard before. It's a good tale, but I don't particularly want to hear it again. I gently mention he is repeating himself, assuming he will stop, apologise and change the subject. He doesn't do that, just shrugs and carries on as if I haven't spoken. It's like starting a tape and not being able to stop it. The 'I've started so I'll finish' scenario.

I look at him, still talking, oblivious, and ask myself 'What am I doing with this man?' My mind drifts off and I imagine flouncing out, such an evocative word, although a bit old fashioned. You need the right clothes, a sufficiency of fabric, a swishy skirt to get the right sort of flounce; the abrupt, curt exit. It would all be wasted on Iain, but this will be our final meal together. Sitting there, Iain's monotone as background, the same old questions are tumbling around. Why had my marriage ended? What had really been going on? How could I have been so naïve? Tears well up. This was not going away.

Of the two conflicting voices inside my head, the critical one declares that in the wider scheme of things my ex-husband's activities were no great deal, not tabloid headlines. The other voice, the supportive one, calmly says, 'Maybe not headlines elsewhere, but to you they were. It was not ordinary but definitely unordinary.' I need help, that is clear, but am unsure what to do.

Serendipity intervenes. I hear that the local University of Galloway is looking for volunteers to join a new research programme called The HindSight Project. It sounds intriguing. Apparently you write about a period from your past that is still having an adverse effect in the present. Yes, I think, that sounds like me. Your writing needs to be faithful to the original feelings, similar to a memoir. Then, with a psychotherapist, you go over these narratives in therapy sessions. The result is having two perspectives on your story; one at the time and one later using hindsight. This allows greater understanding and enables you to begin a healing process. It is an unusual form of counselling. Curious to find out more, I phone for details. In response, I receive the letter as reproduced below.

University of Galloway

School of Counselling and Psychotherapy

THE HINDSIGHT PROJECT:
HOW EFFECTIVE IS NARRATIVE MEMOIR THERAPY?

Explanatory notes for prospective research participants

Dear Sheena,

Thank you for showing an interest in our research project and asking for more details before deciding whether or not you are willing to take part.

Background. Psychotherapy can be a lengthy and time-consuming process. It can take several sessions before the client's story is revealed in detail. The current research project explores an alternative therapeutic method that hopes to show positive results within a shorter time span. Narrative Memoir Therapy combines face-to-face talking therapy with writing about experiences. Both these approaches have proven therapeutic benefits. If you would like to read the background research supporting this project, we can provide a list of references.

Method. A period in the past that is impacting adversely on an individual's current life is chosen. The participant produces a series of ten chronological narratives or chapters about this period as experienced at the time. All the writing is completed before therapy begins. The therapist reads the first narrative only before having their first session with the individual. With hindsight, they explore together what has happened, looking for meanings that were not apparent previously and working to understand motivations for behaviour. The therapist uses theoretical knowledge while the participant uses personal information of themselves and the others involved. There is no looking forward to the next chapter, as no prior information is allowed. The same procedure is repeated for subsequent chapters. Decisions can then be made about the possibilities and value of further therapy.

Confidentiality. The narrative will be read by the therapist only and the normal confidentiality conditions between client and therapist will apply. Both parties will need to agree and sign a consent form.

I shall be happy to help if you have any queries.

Yours sincerely,

Dr David Stephens
NMT Project Director

* * *

I am invited to meet the therapist allocated to me so we can go over the practical details. I feel a little apprenhensive about what is in store. I've a couple of previous experiences with counselling, which had proved useful; the counsellors being great at listening, very calm and relaxed. I think I need a more proactive approach this time, someone to get hold of the issues and shake out all the nuances, welcome and unwelcome.

The University of Galloway is based in a former school

extended and altered to become the university campus. I am directed to Rachael's room in the old part of the building with high ceilings and stone mullioned windows. As I appear in her doorway, she comes from behind the desk to greet me with a welcoming smile. She looks a good bit younger than me, probably mid-forties, informally dressed in trousers, with hair a neat dark bob pushed back to emphasise the pearl studs in her ears. My impression is of someone at peace with themselves emanating a quiet confidence. As we talk, it is clear she is more focused and analytical than the previous counsellors, but I suppose being part of a research department helps with that. We agree a timetable for writing the narratives, one a fortnight ideally, but Rachael appreciates this might not be possible. She warns that some of the writing may be upsetting for me and I can take a break as and when I need. The same applies to the therapy sessions. Usually, they will be once a week, but again it will depend on how I am feeling. Rachael thinks every other week may be more realistic. This is reassuring, as I have been a bit anxious about the logistics. I leave feeling fired up with the prospect of finally reaching some peace, knowing I may have found some answers.

Session One

Unease | Narrative

THERE WAS NOT A CLEAR starting point, a moment that could be identified as setting things up for the fall to come. Relationships don't work like that. Eventually, there may be a last straw, an incident too far, but towards the beginning, it is more like a shifting vagueness. This particular day stayed in my mind and remains very vivid. I suppose it brought home to me that something was not right, but at the time, it was unclear whether that was with me or him or with us.

It started really well, a lovely August day, sunny, warm and full of expectation for enjoyment. Lee and I were off to a classic vehicle show in the grounds of Culzean Castle on the Ayrshire coast. This kind of weather is quite rare in our corner of southwest Scotland, so it was to be savoured and enjoyed to the full. Ideally, a day for an open sports car, but we had to compromise and take my car, with the windows down and the sunroof open. Days of long fair hair blowing around my face were firmly in the past. We had Beth, our rough-coated terrier, perched on my lap, ready to make leaps after enticing sights. Lee drove and I was soon lost in a relaxing semi-doze enjoying the colours of the land. After twenty-six years together, we were comfortable with silence.

We drove north along the Doon Valley with just the occasional dwelling by the road; the green amongst the peat and rock looking deceptively fertile but in reality was coarse grasses and bracken. Meadowsweet and rosebay willow herb grew in abundance in the damp, marshy ground along the burns. Once through Dalmellington, we turned off and drove over open moorland before dropping down through softer country. On the way, we were going to meet up with another couple, Andy and Olive, who knew of a café where bacon rolls and pots of tea were guaranteed. They would be driving their 1951 MG saloon, a Y type in two-tone green and about to be an exhibitor at the show.

We knew each other through the car. Lee worked in wood restoration, ranging from antique furniture to historic timber frames, being currently employed helping to restore Druids, a large country house north of Dumfries. He loved trees and all things wood, not distinguishing between living and dead timber; they were all alive to him. When I saw and felt the patina and subtle shades of polished wood, I could sympathise with his view. Andy seemed to have the same relationship with stone, and he had been brought in to renovate stonework in the house. An interest in real ale helped the friendship along and led to Lee making a beautiful new instrument panel for the MG, out of burled walnut. While Lee and Andy worked with inanimate materials, Olive and I worked with people. She was a librarian and I was self-employed, providing advice to local businesses.

The rendezvous was in a row of white cottages on a quiet hillside street. As we entered the village, Lee said, 'Andy wants me to look at a car with him.'

I shook away the daydream.

'What?'

'It's in Ayr, so we could just take a run up later,' he continued.

'He called me in the week. It seemed a good opportunity to see it. It's an older MG with a wooden frame.'

'Oh,' I supplied.

Part of me argued that yes, it sounded very sensible, as we were near Ayr anyway, but the other part was miserable, the tears prickling. Why didn't he say before, at breakfast, on the way even? Why play these games of withholding stuff to the last minute? 'Why didn't you say before?' I managed. He could tell I was upset.

'What's the matter with you? I'm telling you now.'

I felt the tears pressing behind my eyes as he drew into the kerb to park the car.

'When are you going?'

'We can go after the show.'

'You mean in both cars?'

He looked across at me, irritated now.

'I don't know. What does it matter? It's a good opportunity.'

Without waiting for me, Lee got out of the car to join Andy and Olive as they waved to us before going into the café. I controlled my emotions, the feeling of being left out, forced back the internal protest and prepared to smile my way into the building. Let's face it; it was hardly the end of the world that they wanted to see a car. I trailed behind Lee, blotting my eyes, concentrating on presenting a cheerful face. Why was I feeling like this? But there wasn't time. There were greetings, cheerfulness and bacon rolls being handed round, mugs of tea and chatter about the day. 'What wonderful weather for the show!' We got back in the cars and continued down to the coast.

The show was in the castle grounds, along from the former stable complex, while the castle itself was some distance away, built atop a sheer cliff above the sea. Bordered by mature trees, the show field was an idyllic site on a beautiful summer's day. I remember how important those trees were, voluptuous, deciduous trees in full leaf, forming a textured wall of rich green shades. They exuded a permanence, a link with history, but their continuity was so vulnerable, even on a National Trust for Scotland property. Not being entrants, we bumped over the uneven ground of the parking field next door to get our tickets and park. We gathered up the picnic kit of chairs, rug and baskets from the boot, and with Beth straining at her lead, walked through to find the Y type's spot in the rows of exhibits. The cars were lined up in age order, with a few vintage cars in front with more numerous, younger examples behind. These were the cars of my childhood, which had belonged to friends' parents, Hillman Minx, Jowett Javelin, Standard Vanguard and an Austin Metropolitan. They had seemed more exciting than my father's Morris Oxford; he had a succession of those, always black. Further over, by the parade ring, were a couple of traction engines with the inevitable camp followers of stationary engines phut phut phutting nearby. All around the perimeter were motoring jumble stalls, individual car club stands and a craft tent, providing a busy scene full of buzz and interest, infectious, eclipsing the earlier upset. Andy and Olive had to stay by the car, waiting for the judges, so after leaving our picnic kit in the MG, Lee and I wandered around the show, finding plenty to see and comment on without returning to the previous unease. We both enjoyed traditional rather than modern, which included vehicles of all sorts. We were drawn to the traction engines, savouring their sooty warmth and gentle voices somewhere between a chug and a purr, like a soft metronome. I loved their steamy smell, their coal smutty breath. Sensing their quiet power and solidity, I felt myself relaxing to a calmer state of mind.

I seem to have gone over the top a bit in describing these

machines, but they connected me to the excitement I felt as a young child watching steam railway engines. My mother would take me down the road to a railway bridge where a lane ran down the side of it next to a large goods yard. The mainline trains ran further out, their engines sleek and aloof, but nearer, there were the little tank engines, chugging out their smoke and clanking importantly to move the goods trucks around. They were so alive and of a size a child could relate to, busy but not threatening, the drivers waving at me, so I knew they were my friends. They provided an excitement and sense of adventure, absent in life at home.

We returned to the car to find it sporting a blue rosette, so smiles all round. Olive and I had divided up the lunch responsibilities and between us had devised a good feast. A cool box in their car provided salads, cold meats and chilled wine while I provided artisan bread, homemade sausage and egg pie, cheese and savoury nibbles. Olive produced a box of her meringues, complete with a bowl of whipped cream for self-assembly. These were something to swoon over, the crisp collapsibility of them contrasting with the soft chewy inside. There we were, gathered round the boot of the car with our folding chairs and wooden table, sipping wine in the sunshine, surrounded by beautiful elderly cars. They had so much more personality than the modern versions, although nothing could surpass the quality and appeal of the even older vintage vehicles in the rows before us. I still have a photo of that day, Lee and I sitting back in our folding chairs. He is holding his wine glass upside down with a ruthful smile at its emptiness, with Beth's lead hooked round a chair leg while she snoozes in the shade. Empty plates lie scattered over the rug between the chairs.

It must have been after this that the car visit was brought up again, and it became obvious the course of action had already been decided. Alcohol and sunshine is not a good mixture, and perhaps that lowered my tolerance level, as I felt left out, excluded, uncertain of what was going on. Dimly, I realised that I was overreacting, like clutching at insubstantial shapes in a fog, but was unable to stop. Tension rose up, threatening to overwhelm my capacity for control. I wanted to shout and to throw things in a proper toddler-style tantrum. How satisfying it must be to hurl glass and crockery around and hear it smash, and incongruously, at the height of this pressure, I inwardly laughed at the absurdity and futility of hurling plastic plates and cutlery around, even the glasses were plastic. They would refuse to be hurled and just flutter impotently to the ground without ever reaching a trajectory. This distraction was short-lived, upbringing prevented an outburst, but in the emotion of the moment, I got up abruptly, not trusting myself to speak, and walked briskly away. I sensed Andy and Olive's eyes following me, surprised, but Lee did not look up.

I went through the entrance nearest us, crossed a small car park and through to the courtyard, surrounded by the former stables and coach houses for the castle, now an information centre, shop, café and toilets. I went to the ladies' and straight into a cubicle. Jeans and knickers round my knees, a trickle of pee, no real need but an automatic response. The real need was a private place to cry, and the tears came, soundlessly. How often do women use cubicles as a refuge, to hide away for a few blissful moments to recharge, reassess or just have a greet? I waited until no one was outside the cubicles before emerging, walking past the shop, then crossing a patch of grass bounded by a wall, with the sea beyond and a sheer drop to the rocky shore below. I stood there, looking out to the granite bump of Ailsa Craig and the Mull of Kintyre.

From an early age, I had been drawn to the sea in all its

moods; there is something intensely soothing about gazing out to sea. I had done it as a teenager, to loosen the knots of angst, and I felt my knots ease now as the ropes of tension streamed out in a line, straight towards the horizon, and then, dropping over the edge, releasing the pressure as they went. My thoughts were twirling outwards too, dissipating harmlessly in the depth of water. The sea provides an extra dimension, away from yourself, its power reducing you to insignificance. No one can stop those waves, they just come on and on and there is comfort in knowing that humans are not in control. Standing by that wall, I wasn't thinking any particular thoughts, just absorbing and building back some energy.

I don't know how long I remained there, but I eventually heard my name spoken nearby. It was Olive, looking worried and smiling tentatively. What a neurotic, self-centred person she must think I am. I smiled back, grateful for her presence.

'I'm sorry, Olive,' I said. 'Don't quite know what happened, hormones probably.'

I clutched at that ubiquitous excuse: I was too old for 'time of the month' and the menopause was stretching it a bit, as I was sixty-one; HRT perhaps, but it was a useful excuse. She looked relieved.

'Yes, I thought it was something like that. We were worried about you.'

I turned away from the wall and walked back with her to the showground.

'The men have gone to look at the jumble stuff,' she said, 'so what about going round the craft tent?'

I was happy to put off facing Lee for a bit, so readily agreed. When we finally met up, nothing was said about the car visit and all seemed normal. Olive produced flasks of tea and shortly after that the showground was emptying. The trip home was made in silence, but the companionship of the journey out was missing. I felt lonely and depressed.

Once home, the routine tasks of feeding animals and ourselves were carried out with polite exchanges, but I was bothered by my reaction and phoned to make a doctor's appointment. Maybe there was something physically wrong, or just another manifestation of the long-standing emotional difficulties with the relationship with my mother. Later in the week, the doctor was sympathetic. She knew I wouldn't bother her unless I was really concerned, so I was checked out and bloods were taken for testing. She then said they had a counsellor attached to the practice for a few months, would I like an appointment. I agreed, thinking it might help get to the bottom of my eccentric behaviour.

Unease | Therapy

Rachael. Welcome to our first appointment, Sheena, and congratulations on completing the ten narratives. They must have taken a considerable amount of time and effort. I hope we can do them justice, I sincerely hope that. We set the ground rules at our introduction meeting, but to recap, the plan is to work together to tease out what happened during the breakdown of your marriage and hopefully help you gain a deeper insight into both Lee's behaviour and your reaction to it.

Sheena. That would be good, as I feel I'm at a stage now when I need to face up to what happened and accept my part in it.

R. OK. So, each piece centres on an event important in the timeline tracking your changing relationship with Lee, and I've read your first story, which is the starting point. It could've been simply a description of an enjoyable day out, but two things happened that turned it into something more. So let's unpick that, and on the way I'll get a better idea of the two of you as individuals and as a couple. During the journey to the show, it sounds as though you were easy in each other's company without words being needed. Was that typical?

S. Yes, early on in our marriage there seemed to be some tacit agreement that we could be comfortable without speaking. We weren't chatterers.

R. OK, you sat through breakfast, went through that journey and then out of the blue, he says, 'I'm going to look at a car.' It's not the car though, is it? I think we can safely say that. So let's freeze that moment. I don't pick up any hint of indignation or anger, no 'what the hell is he playing at?' 'What right has he to go off without telling me?' Let's find out what it was. Can you relive your feelings before the tears started pricking? What was your immediate emotional response?

S. Well, it was like, like having a fist in your chest – *wumph*. It was almost making me want to step back, but of course I couldn't because of the seatback, but it had that sort of effect, and immediately following that, I felt sort of desolate, as if I was on the outside, being excluded. And it sounded like it was deliberate, why didn't he tell me before? It would have been such a natural thing to do. This was playing games, a deliberate deceit. Yes, I know it sounds like a gross over-reaction, but that's how it was. Looking back now, it just seems ridiculous.

R. It is not ridiculous. It's how you genuinely felt and that is what's important. Whether anyone else may have thought it ridiculous is utterly irrelevant, this is about you and a very real emotional effect. If we have a reaction that appears to be stronger than the situation merits, it can be an indication of some early experience that is unresolved. I wonder if your response is tuning into something that has happened before. Is that a familiar feeling? That games are being played, that you can't rely on what someone is telling you?

S. Yes, yes, I suppose it is. It goes right back, because I couldn't trust my mother. How clichéd is that? One day she would praise you for some thing and the next day criticise you for exactly the same thing. You were always on tenterhooks, not knowing what mood she would be in, you couldn't trust, you couldn't rely on anything. And because you were on your own, no brothers or sisters, you only had yourself to fall back on; didn't know whether you could trust anyone else. So I suppose I've got this entrenched feeling of vulnerability, don't know what else you would call it. Wow! Where did all that come from? Sorry.

R. I sense a longstanding pain and I don't think we should go too deeply into this in the first session. Would you like to pause for a minute or two?

S. No, I'm OK. It's made me realise how sensitive I am to not knowing where I stand with somebody. I must have been particularly susceptible that day, don't know why.

R. OK, let's look at words, at talking. You say he didn't tell you about the car visit, but how typical was this of him anyway? Was he good at sharing everyday stuff with you?

S. No, it was like pulling hen's teeth sometimes. He wasn't very good at talking. He tended to save his words up before carefully measuring them out, at a time of his choosing. A deceitful way with words really, using their absence to deceive. But in the right mood, with his smile, I forgave him for the lack of words.

R. Mmm, I'm wondering what's happening here. The fact he didn't tell you about the car trip doesn't sound as if this would have surprised you particularly. You reacted strongly though. Had there been something else going on to make you more vulnerable?

S. Not that I remember, no. I was feeling particularly sensitive and I think that is why the whole day stuck in my memory. I seemed to have a heightened awareness of everything, as you can tell by how I went a bit over the top about trees, steam engines, the sea, meringues even.

R. You relaxed on the journey though, dozing you said, so perhaps your defences dropped a bit and allowed in a greater emotional engagement. Anyway, we haven't got enough information yet. Let's take a different angle. In order to avoid your reaction then and later, what could Lee have done to defuse the situation?

S. I suppose I hoped that he would engage with me, acknowledge that not telling me was a mistake but reassure me it hadn't been deliberate. He could then have said, 'Let's go into the café and discuss the best plan with Andy and Olive.' That would have made it all OK. I know I tend to get emotional, get things out of proportion and then wonder what all the fuss was about. A peak of intensity and then it suddenly disappears, snow off a dyke kind of effect, and you're left wondering if you saw the snow at all. But in the emotion of the moment, the snow is very real. He'd known me long enough to know what I was like. Perhaps I hoped for a bit more understanding.

R. And that brings us to the second event. You give various options for dealing with this sudden immense pressure inside you, but you manage it and go off to be alone. In the first episode, you also managed to control your response and put on a social face. This takes a lot of inner strength and energy and, I suspect, a lot of practice. Would you agree with that?

S. Don't know, I mean it's just what you do. I've always done it, so I suppose it's second nature now.

R. You talk about wanting to throw the cutlery around and I like the idea that plastic is no good for a dramatic effect. Do I detect a hint of wistfulness here?

S. Yes, probably, appeals to the child in me. Once, I was expelled from a play group for throwing another child's toys over the garden wall. As an only child, I wasn't used to being with other children, so would have been feeling uncomfortable, another way of getting rid of emotion, I suppose.

R. You say that upbringing prevented an outburst. What's behind that?

S. Mmmm. Well, if I did have a dramatic performance, I think that a split second after an outburst, I would be overcome with shame.

R. Shame because...?

S. At letting others down, letting myself down.

R. That's a rational explanation, but I wonder if there's another one. Are we talking about shame or protection here, protection from being challenged? After all, if we don't expose ourselves, we can stay safe.

S. I think there's a mixture. Obviously, there's childhood diktats of 'we do not misbehave in public', 'stop it, someone may see you', etc. Probably fear too, as just thinking about it is making me anxious. By making a public exhibition of myself, I am exposing my private self; my personal integrity is under threat. Sorry, that sounds a bit heavy doesn't it. Like you have just said, keeping things to myself protects me from ridicule, but then I am ashamed of being wimpish and just slinking away. At the show, there was the three of them, all knowing, all in on the arrangements and me on the outside. I did what I always do in those situations, I walked away to gain time on my own. Put the shouts back in their box and let the tears shout instead.

R. And you have your own methods to cope. Being on your own and using the sea seem to be your ways of coping. We all develop our own defensive strategies against emotions and events that threaten to overwhelm us. Yours seem to work well for you.

S. Yes, that's true, I suppose. I am prone to mood swings and have a need to be alone. Retreating into myself is second nature, but then that's true for Lee too. We tolerated and respected our individual needs for retreat. We were compatible in that, as in so many other ways, so a certain mutuality of needs.

R. In the narrative, you spent a lot of time looking out to sea but not really thinking much.

S. I was feeling rather than thinking. It's doubtful I articulated it as I have in the narrative. What I'm trying to do there is put the feelings into words so I can communicate them. I had a keen sense of being alone, not lonely but alone, which of course is a familiar feeling. Probably more a suspension of thoughts and time; a pervading melancholia.

R. You end your narrative by saying the doctor recommended you see a counsellor. So, as the reader, I am left wondering what happened.

S. Yes, I went to see the counsellor, Diane, for a few sessions. I thought the root of my problem was my relationship with my mother, as I mentioned before, so she agreed to concentrate on that. It was more about me talking and having the chance to spill it all out to someone not involved, who didn't know my mother or me. I found that helpful and… liberating.

R. Good, sounds as though that really helped. Your mother has been mentioned a few times now and I suspect will be again. I don't, at the moment, want to go into detail, as I said earlier. But are you able to give the gist of the mother issue.

S. Yes, alright, here goes. An only child of undemonstrative parents with no extended family or friends after moving abroad when very young. It is no surprise that I became very independent and self-reliant. When my mother didn't get her way, we had psychological warfare, tearful accusations and long periods of silence. She wanted a 'normal' little girl, but I was a tomboy. There were clashes galore, especially as I got older, but I always won. She never learned. My father was no help, as he either took her side or stayed out of the way. She was a selfish, manipulative woman, spoilt, quick to criticise and very slow to praise unless you had done something that she approved of. I don't think she could show affection and instead showed her love for me, an obsessional love, by spending money on material things to an embarrassing degree. Will that do?

R. Yes, at least from the outside. It also suggests an awful lot that is not said. Now, I think we are beginning to see why this episode is important. It has provided a small pathway into your unconscious, which is influencing your conscious life. We need to take time over this, to reveal the hidden part of your life very carefully, no breaking down doors and storming in but very slowly, cautiously. We'll work on this over the next few weeks.

We're coming up to the time we need to finish. Before we do, could I ask you if there is anything you would like to comment on, anything you would like to do differently?

S. No, I feel OK with being here, although I appreciate some of it will be difficult. This method does seem to get to the heart of things pretty quickly though, doesn't it, which I like, actually. I'm not one for waffle and tiptoeing around.

R. Yes, I realise that. In a conventional session, we would have talked more generally in the first meeting, but we've bypassed much of that by having the narrative first. It does make things more demanding and not all people would welcome that.

Session Two

Suspicion | Narrative

THE FIRST NARRATIVE INTRODUCED LEE and I without background or context. I need to rectify that before continuing with the next episode, as it helps to get the future narratives in perspective.

Lee and I met at university. He had started at the usual age while, being twenty-eight, I was classed as a mature student. I wasn't bothered about actual age, so the difference was never a problem. At the end of my first year and Lee's second, we happened to be on the same vacation job and were joined by another student, Phil. The three of us spent the summer travelling round in a Landrover, measuring archaeological sites for a Berkshire museum with Steven, one of the curators, to guide us. It amused him that our lunch stops were determined by consulting the Good Beer Guide. Fortunately, all three of us had a serious interest in real ale, but as Lee came from a city background, beer-drinking women were something of a curiosity. Our area had a high density of qualifying pubs in country locations, so we could sit outside in the sunshine drinking beer and eating homemade sandwiches. It was a memorable time of fun and friendship without any emotional complications. This suited me very well, as I was going through divorce proceedings.

During the following winter, my relationship with Lee progressed, so that some years later, we were married and busy renovating a cottage in Sussex. Neither of us had roots in any particular place, so the next move, a few years later, was about finding somewhere affordable with more space, land and buildings. After a recce holiday, we decided that we liked Herefordshire, so that's where we went, to a property a few miles outside Hereford. It was a nineteenth century brick cottage in a green nook, bordered by mature hedges, an orchard of knarled and lichened apple trees plus two acres of pasture. There was the obligatory cider mill, long disused, and a range of outbuildings comfortably sagging. Building societies would have been put off by the damp and neglect, but we could buy it outright, just, with the proceeds from our previous venture. To many, it would have looked a wreck requiring far too much work to put right. Not to us, we loved its mellowed brick walls and mossed slate roof. It had been allowed the time to meld with its own niche and have the freedom to be itself, moulded by years and the natural order. Some people would have set about with PVC window replacements and extensions, but we just let things be, allowing a degree of gentle chaos, valuing restraint and respect rather than dominance.

I managed to find a part-time job in Hereford in a microbiology lab, my original training, while Lee stayed at home doing a lot of the renovation work. His original degree had been building construction, with a strong emphasis on conservation and restoration allowing him to indulge his particular passion for wood. Before the move, Lee had opted out of a mainstream job to follow the self-employed route and continued this in Herefordshire. The hours and money were more erratic, obviously, but he felt more in charge and that was important. I was fully supportive and not particularly worried about the finance side; there was only ourselves to consider, as children had never been on the agenda. I believe in everyone following their own path rather than just taking the safe option of a 'proper job'. The antithesis of my parents' philosophy in which security, safety and pensions were paramount.

Once the main repairs were completed, Lee created an income ranging from restoring timber in listed houses to repairing furniture for local antique dealers. Like many small business people, he was great at the doing but not so good at keeping track of the money. I took a business management course to give practical support to Lee, later extending this to help local small firms with business plans and financial advice and eventually replacing the lab job.

Our lifestyle was pretty frugal, paying more than lip service to the 'good life' ethic. My contribution was in the kitchen and garden, allowing me to indulge a fondness for poultry by breeding pure Welsummers and Marans, selling the deep brown eggs as well as young birds. They had arks in the orchard and warm sheds in the winter with a few favourites pottering freely around the buildings. I loved their gentle murmur and chuntering as they focused on the ground around them and the happy, uninhibited way they dust bathed in the sun. To utilise the pasture, I had a small flock of Portland sheep, little white-faced jobs, for the animal interest and to provide us with lamb for the freezer.

After eight years, we got restless again and started thinking about moving. The outside work was becoming a burden rather than a pleasure, so downsizing was a sensible way to go. The idea of Scotland came out of the blue, but once implanted, it seemed the obvious choice. In my case, moving to Scotland felt like going home, as much as I felt at home anywhere. My father was Scottish, so I used to have family there. The next decision was which part of Scotland?

Neither of us had a job to go to or any business contacts, but we had enough money from the house sale to see us through a few months. We both agreed it had to be an area with trees, which ruled out a lot of the Highlands, as coniferous monoculture did not count. The South West suited well, being in easy reach of motorways if Lee needed to travel for sourcing materials. We couldn't afford anything really old or special, but even humble dwellings can have a sense of history and time. We settled for a small stone cottage on a hillside above the Solway Firth, looking down on the village below.

Garden Cottage was built with quality materials and some style, as in a previous incarnation it had been the gardener's cottage to an imposing sandstone house in gothic mode next door. It had a part walled garden in poor shape, mature trees on the boundary and some outbuildings with plenty of potential. The land at the back began on the level before sloping quite steeply downhill, giving a wide view out over the estuary. The cottage looked a bit miserable; it had had little maintenance in recent years, but the essentials were there. Upstairs it had dormer windows and coved ceilings, while downstairs there was a kitchen big enough for our pine table and a living room along the back with two further rooms destined to become our den and dining room respectively. We loved living there and never regretted putting in the work to transform it into a cosy home.

Shortly after Lee had completed the essential work, he was very lucky, serendipity personified. During an encounter in the pub, it came up that Lee was a wood conservationist. Somebody mentioned an estate north of Dumfries seeking help to renovate the timber fittings and furniture in an old house. Apparently, there had been an advert in *The Herald*, and someone else volunteered that the relevant copy was still in the recycle pile. A quick visit on the way home to retrieve it and there it was. It sounded really promising, although, typically, Lee was a bit sceptical. He applied and was invited to an interview at the house. He came back full of enthusiasm about the project, leaving behind his former despondency and self-doubt. He'd been offered the job, and in a rare loquacious mood, he spent the evening telling me about it over supper and a bottle of wine.

Originally, Druids was a sandstone country house, but around the late 1890s, the then owners decided to redesign and extend the original house in the fashionable Arts and Crafts style. That caught my interest, as the asymmetry of those designs appealed, with their quirky features. Evidently, the building had been re-roofed, the upper storey skimmed and painted off-white, with brick and stone extensions added each side, asymmetrically; one with a two-storey bay window. Lee had photos of the present house and it was obvious the blending of brick, stone and timber, old with new, was a surprising success. Druids was category A listed, with all the attendant responsibilities, but it had deteriorated. The house was owned by a foundation, the Logie Trust, based in Glasgow with connections to Dumfries. Currently, extensive renovations were under way. The job description was to renovate the main interior, including the original furniture. A lot of basic work had been done, but now the aim was to open parts to the public and find other uses. Lee seemed perfectly happy to abandon self-employment for a regular income and an opportunity to capitalise on his many talents.

I had a rather different approach. When we first arrived in Scotland, I found a couple of part-time office jobs, basic stuff, but it was a way in, to get to know people and make connections. After a while, I met a business consultant, Alan, who was working with the local business development company. He gave me bits of work, but as he got busier gave me local jobs while concentrating on larger projects in the west of the region. I picked up a few clients of my own too through word of mouth, so was pulling my weight financially, although not working full time. I was vaguely aware that our lives were taking a divergent path, particularly in Lee's case. Hopefully, that will be enough background for now. I shall move on to the next episode in late September of the same year, 2004.

Lee left for work about 8.15 each morning, but being self-employed, I had hours that were more flexible. On this particular day, while Lee finished dressing and bathrooming, I went downstairs in my dressing gown to get the breakfast rituals underway. Beth went straight to the back door, jumping around with her 'I'm getting desperate, open that door NOW' look. I filled the kettle with water and switched it on. Breakfast consisted of toast and jam, so I put bread in the toaster and got the rest of the kit out of the fridge. By the time the second batch of toast was on, the kettle boiled, tea brewed, Lee was downstairs. Beth was now on lookout duty for any toast crusts heading her way. We were not usually very talkative in the morning, mainly because any attempts by me at conversation were met with silence.

At breakfast, I had learnt to restrict myself to mundane issues of coming home time and shopping. Earlier was different though, as I invariably woke up in the morning with swirling thoughts, questions and ideas that had been in gestation during sleep, now jostling to be heard. Not everyone wants original and controversial views, on anything from American aggression, grubbing up hedgerows or the design of shampoo bottles, that early in the morning. My rant of the day never lasted for long, a minute at the most probably. Lee was the only recipient and usually joined in, finding it all entertaining. It took a few minutes to expend all the energy and then all was calm. At one time, he had a very good way of shutting me down, an early morning quickie, which diverted me very efficiently. I was vaguely aware that it had been a while since we had done that.

While munching toast, Lee asked where I was going that day and I replied, 'Near New Galloway,' then remembered I would need to buy some lunch from the shop there but had no cash and wouldn't be going near a machine.

'Just thought, I have no cash. Could you lend me some, please?'

'Yes, of course, help yourself. My wallet and stuff is still upstairs.'

To make sure I didn't forget, I went straight up to the bedroom and picked up his wallet from beside the bed, flipped it open and took out a ten pound note. At the same time, a slip of paper fell out, a folded over till receipt by the look of it. Picking it up, I expected it to be from a local garage, but instead it said 'Discovery Quay Motor Inn, Dundee'. The date was the previous weekend and the amount was £49. I stood there frozen. What on earth was this about? In one of those weird flashes of illogical, fantastical thinking, I remembered we had visited Discovery Quay some months before on the way back from a holiday. We had both wanted to tour Shackleton's Arctic ship, and in some crazy way, I thought he had gone back there. It would have been feasible, as I had been down south the previous weekend visiting my mother. All this took several seconds and there was no time for further explorations. I needed to get back downstairs. I replaced the receipt in the wallet, picked up his keys and phone and returned to the kitchen, where I merely handed Lee the wallet and thanked him for the loan. Soon after that, he was off, leaving me to pour another cup of tea and climb slowly back to bed, head whirling at each step amid total confusion.

Beth thought bed was a great idea and settled herself around my feet. My heart rate would not slow down. What on earth was going on? My original idea, that he had taken himself off to revisit the Discovery museum ship was farcical. He hadn't mentioned going anywhere on my return. He'd given some detail about a walk taken with Beth but that was only one day accounted for. None the wiser, I sipped my tea. And then, breaking through the musings, as if it had been bobbing about just below the surface waiting for an opportunity, came a name, Chloe. Of course, Chloe the legal and HR manager, who had moved down from Glasgow with Richard Logie when he became director at Druids. I pictured her. Short and curvy, neat dark hair, smartly dressed but rather cool in manner. But where did that suspicion come from? I was aware that Lee and Chloe got on well. She had been supportive from the beginning, as her long knowledge of the Foundation had helped Lee ease into his new role. I had met her a few times, when calling at Druids for one reason or another.

I thought back and conjured up in my mind a particular afternoon. I was in the office Lee shared with the project manager, Ken. Standing at the bookcase behind his desk, as Lee finished a phone call, I wouldn't have been visible from outside. Chloe came along the terrace leading to the half-glazed door at the back of the office. Through the glass, I could see her approach and watched her look directly at Lee with an expectant smile on her face. She came through the door, making straight for his desk, but he was still on the phone. When she saw me, the smile instantly disappeared. She veered off, across the room and out of the internal door into the main building. Alarm bells started to ring but were silenced as Lee came off the phone. I didn't think any more about it but now remembered the times her name came up in conversation, Chloe this and Chloe that.

He'd accompanied her to the infirmary in Dumfries when she'd had a minor accident that needed stitching. Why did he have to go? Wouldn't it be more natural for Alison, the director's PA, or Sandra in reception to go? And there was the time I phoned his mobile late one afternoon to remind him about something. The phone was answered by a woman, 'This is Lee's phone.' I asked if Lee was there and said who I was. She confirmed she was Chloe and said Lee was driving as they were coming back from Carlisle. She took my message but with no pleasantries at all.

I went back to pondering Dundee and fetched a road atlas from downstairs to get a clearer picture of location and distances. I noticed it wasn't very far from Perth and remembered Lee mentioning that Chloe's mother lived there. Had she used a visit to her mother to nip over to Dundee? She was married, so was not necessarily available for overnight excursions. I made myself stop there, I needed to get myself dressed and out. All this speculating was getting nowhere, more evidence was required.

Over the next few weeks, neither of us was away overnight. Of course, that didn't mean there was nothing happening. Chloe lived in Dumfries, so my imagination was dreaming up quick liaisons at her house during lunchtime. Then one Monday, Alan emailed to ask if I could be at a meeting and workshop in Stranraer the next Friday. It would go on into the evening, so he suggested I stay overnight with him and his family. I had done that before, so readily accepted. Driving sixty-odd miles in the dark was not pleasant, with streams of lorries heading for the ferry, dazzling with their lights. As soon as the email had whooshed off, I thought: this could be another opportunity for Lee.

The following Saturday afternoon, I arrived back home and there was no hint that he had been away. I was in a dilemma. Had he or hadn't he? He seemed to keep his wallet with him, so there was no opportunity to find more receipts, but another possibility occurred to me. The weather had turned colder, so Lee was wearing a thicker outer jacket, hanging it up by the front door, as the backdoor hooks were for workaday coats, waterproofs and overalls. On the Sunday evening, he went out to the workshop to finish some job, allowing me to slip into the hallway. I felt in the pockets of Lee's coat and in an inside one found a sheet of A4 paper folded over. A quick glance told me it was a reservation for the same Discovery Quay Motor Inn, but it was a booking, not proof that he had actually been. It was something though, and any hopes that the first receipt had been an aberration and could sink down into oblivion were finally shattered.

I needed to share all this with someone and there was one obvious choice. We had met Jane and Robert in Herefordshire and had maintained contact despite their move to Cumbria. A year earlier they had moved to Scotland and now lived in Castle Douglas. Jane was the area organiser for a national cancer charity with an office in Dumfries, so we sometimes snatched a coffee or lunch if I was in town. On Monday, I phoned her, as I was working in Dumfries that day.

'Come to the office,' she said. 'I'm on my own except for Linda on phone duty.'

I arrived late morning and Jane came to the door to let me in. She took one look and said 'I think coffee's required. You're in luck. I've got the machine on the go.'

Coffee did help and the whole story came spilling out. It sounded a bit pathetic to my ears, but she took it all without exclamations or throwing up of hands. She was used to dealing with emotional crises, so took the practical approach.

'So,' she said, 'we don't know whether Lee actually went there.'

'No,' I agreed, watching her tapping away on her keyboard.

Evidently, she was finding the website of the Discovery Quay inn. She turned to me with a determined smile, 'Let's find out.' She picked up her phone and got through to the inn, saying she was calling from Lee's work, that he had been booked in for Friday and asked if he was still there, as they wanted to contact him. She listened, thanked them and put the phone down.

'He was there on Friday but left Saturday morning. What on earth is he up to? Why Dundee?'

'Exactly,' I answered. 'It's all very odd. Also, that booking was a computer printout of an email. I know he doesn't use my computer, but do you think he has a laptop in the workshop at home?'

Jane thought for a while and then said he had a computer at work.

'Well, yes, of course,' I said dismissively. 'He has one on his desk in the office, but that would be far too risky. People could be coming or going anytime and could see what he was doing.'

'No,' Jane replied, shaking her head. 'Not that one. He's got one in the workshop in the outbuildings. I don't think you were there, but shortly after we moved up here, Robert was asking about Druids and Lee invited us to look round. He showed us his workshop in the buildings behind the house, and in the back of that, there was a small room with a desk and a computer. With the inner door shut, no one could see, as the only window was across the back wall and high up. He had a little den, kettle and tea kit as well. At the time, I was amused by that.'

I looked at her, astonished. I had been shown round Druids too, had the workshop pointed out to me, but I had no idea about this little den.

'Good grief, is that what's been happening?' I exclaimed.

'Well, it seems like a plausible answer, doesn't it?'

'Yes, but even so, I think I'll have a look in the workshop at home. There could be some other evidence. What if he has a stack of bulk-buy condoms hidden away in there? Although even in bulk they wouldn't take up much space, would they?'

And that bizarre thought provided enough light relief to ease the tension in me. We had a good laugh, proper laughs rather than superficial giggles.

Suspicion | Therapy

Rachael. This is slightly different from the previous piece, as you give a mixture of background and story. It broadens the information we have about both of you, giving a more rounded picture. In Herefordshire, I get a strong sense that you were partners, friends and that you relied on each other quite extensively. Does that sound reasonable?

Sheena. Yes, I was trying to give a feeling about our lives there. I look back and regard it as, basically, a very good time. We had somewhere that was very definitely ours, a secure little retreat where we could express our own personalities. Lee had his workshop all sorted, and I had a few ewes in the orchard and the poultry. At that time, we had two dogs, two cats, and yes, it was good. We each had our own interests while on the same property. Apart but together as it were, but helping each other with practical tasks when two pairs of hands were needed. Sometimes if Lee finished his work before me, he'd bring a glass of beer and sit in the shed where I was working, with young chicks, for instance. I loved rearing the chicks, I got a lot of satisfaction hearing them cheeping away, healthy and content.

R. Yes, you may not be maternally inclined, but you have a strong nurturing instinct. I think it could be appropriate to explore this a bit further here. You mention that you both agreed not to have children. Fair enough. Possibly premature to ask the question how you reached that decision, but I don't want it lurking in the background unanswered.

S. Yes, I see the sense in that. Shall I go over the reasons?

R. Yes, please, if you are OK to do that.

S. I can't remember ever being actively interested in children. I wasn't one of those little girls who enjoy trundling proudly around with their dolls in a pram. My mother came to realise that clockwork trains were much more appreciated; I was a tomboy. I've never felt at ease with babies, regarding them as too messy and noisy, at both ends. I just don't have anything like the dedication and commitment required for creating and bringing up children. I respect people who do and certainly appreciate that I am out on a limb. I don't expect everyone to agree with me.

R. You may not be in the majority, but you are far from being alone in those views. Good though, that you had the honesty to recognise that children are not for you.

S. It sounds perverse, I suppose, but I do feel very strongly that if you have children, you do so by choice, are absolutely prepared to put in all the work and all the love that's required. I regard this as vital because children don't just belong to parents but to a whole generation.

R. Every child a wanted child. If only. Interesting you bring in the idea of generation because, of course, the positive and negative effects of parenting can carry through to future generations, an enormous responsibility.

S. Yes, I do see it that way, but then it is easier for me, as I lack the biological drive to reproduce. I think that's at the heart of it, although I can give all sorts of rational explanations, such as over-population. I think my mother had me simply because married women had babies, it was expected of them. I don't think she had any great commitment to motherhood, so maybe my lack of interest has a genetic base.

R. And Lee, what were his reasons?

S. Well, he didn't seem to have any ambitions re fatherhood. His mother had had another baby when he was about twelve, so he knew all the practical implications and didn't want a repeat. Early on, Lee had stated categorically that he did not want children, so we had full agreement there.

R. Some women who choose to be childless are hassled, ostracised almost, by other women. Did you ever experience that?

S. Yes, I've read of that, but I haven't experienced it. Being on the outside, regarded as different, I may not have noticed anyway. When the inevitable question arises, I just say no, by choice, and leave it at that. Nowadays, of course, it's questions about grandchildren. There was a time when my mother would make unsubtle hints, as her friends were now grandparents and she felt left out, lacking in status. I doubt she would have been interested in the reality, and years later, she actually admitted that.

R. No children means there is more focus on being a couple without dilution or deflection. From clients, I have seen how children turn a couple into a triangle. Of course, to most people, this is what family means, and they rejoice in it, but couple life can become eroded. You and Lee took a different path, so what implications were there?

S. A greater reliance and focus on each other, so I suppose we had a more intensive, undiluted couple relationship. We had the freedom not to grow up, with a mature appreciation of not letting go entirely of childhood. Being childlike, not childish. We were able to drift back to the uncomplicated enjoyment of simple things, which is one of the few benefits of childhood; having fun, in other words.

R. Yes, this follows on from earlier when you were describing your lives in Herefordshire. I am seeing a picture of the two of you forming a different type of triangle, not with children but with your home as security against the world outside.

S. Looking back, I realise we tended to be quite insular, but I don't want to give the impression we lived like hermits. There were Lee's customers, who often became friends as well, especially the antique dealers. I had people coming to buy pullets and eggs and I was drawn into the local Good Lifers network or leather sandals brigade, as Lee called them. I thought sometimes that we should widen our horizons a bit, make more effort socially, but he was content as things were. He would go along with any social arrangements, having people in for supper, for instance, but not initiate it.

R. Right. Let's move on then. After the move to Scotland, you had a very different lifestyle. Previously, Lee had given up full-time employment to become self-employed. Now he has taken on full-time employment again, so I'm wondering if he felt any resentment about that.

S. No, I don't think he resented it. In a funny sort of way, he actually liked being employed again; it took the pressure off him. I know he found self-employment difficult sometimes. There were periods when money was tight, which made him feel vulnerable, as he took responsibility seriously. I think he was glad to be away from that, certainly more than I was. I always assumed that we would manage somehow, by luck or wits, for the simple reason that that has been my experience of life. I expect that something will turn up, because it always has, with the proviso that you are proactive and positive in searching for a solution. Lee had a different philosophy, but he knew what it was like to do without, as his mother had struggled bringing up children on her own. I never had any financial insecurities, because I knew my parents would always bail me out, albeit reluctantly.

R. So that is the background, and I imagine the implications of it will feed in to the sessions to come. I suggest we move on now to the next part of the story and that troublesome little piece of paper. In the previous narrative, you hinted that Lee wasn't very good at talking about things, a bit secretive, and here we have a potentially massive secret, but is it? Let's look at the moment you found that receipt. You were not snooping, you had his permission to go to his wallet and take some money. The receipt fell out and you read it. A perfectly normal response. What I don't understand is... what you could have done was pick up the receipt, go downstairs and ask 'Hey, what's this?' Wouldn't that have been a natural thing to do? But you didn't. Why?

S. Yes, good question. I don't think I look for confrontation particularly, not in personal relationships, so I would have avoided that. Not asking is safer, after all. If I had asked, it would've meant I had read the receipt, putting me in the wrong. He would've resented that and possibly lied. I couldn't simply assume he would tell the truth if challenged. He may well have got annoyed or been dismissive.

R. Yes, but you don't come over as a particularly timid person, so I'm wondering if this goes deeper. If you feel strongly about something, I think you would say so.

S. Well, I probably tried to rationalise it at the time. I mean, if I'd asked for an explanation, he would have given me a reasonable-sounding story. That could have left me feeling like it didn't sound right, but that I couldn't challenge him further.

R. He doesn't know that you found the receipt. Can you imagine him downstairs suddenly realising that the receipt was there. Were you going to find it? How was he going to explain it away? Nevertheless, he was saved, you didn't ask and didn't confront him and... Just thinking, is this going right back, to what you mentioned before? You're an only child with parents you didn't really trust, so would you probably have been cautious around them, not questioning?

S. Yes, I suppose that could tie in, but not sure how yet. I can't actually remember any situation when I could just turn to them and share, and this is about sharing, isn't it? Being comfortable enough to ask if something is bothering you. I didn't know how to share, never had to, not sharing toys or sharing a room, so I would have found that difficult.

R. OK, so where are we now? You've suggested that you would have found confrontation uncomfortable, but you also mentioned Lee may have lied to you. There seems to be an assumption he would have lied. Where does that leave you?

S. Well, it's pushing me back onto my own resources again. I wouldn't have known where I was. I wouldn't have known if he was telling the truth or not.

R. Yes, why is that important?

S. Because… when you don't know it's true, when it's just suspicion, there is hope that maybe it's not true. But when you know it's true, you haven't really got much choice in the matter, you have to face up to it, to being excluded again.

R. Yes, and do you think that takes us back to the first story? Are there similar feelings?

S. I suppose it does, yes, hadn't thought of that. Those feelings are similar and so familiar.

R. This is all getting a bit circular though, isn't it? I can't help thinking there is some wriggling on the hook here. What we have is an example of an apparently trivial incident but which actually has far deeper significance, and I do not mean the possibility of cheating on you is trivial. Up to this point, you have trusted this man, you are very close, as neither of you has family support, you are each other's family and now that bond is under threat. But at the moment, it could all be speculation. There is no proof that anything untoward is happening, and yet, apparently, that possibility is ignored.

You have noticed this woman, Chloe, but haven't considered anyone else, seeming to set her up for the role. You recalled when you saw her at work and a couple of other occasions that you thought a bit odd at the time. Do you think, consciously or not, that you had become a bit worried, threatened even, or is that too strong a word?

S. Yes, that is too strong. Possibly a kind of below the surface awareness, the antennae twitching but no actual threat recognised.

R. The antennae twitching, as you put it, is something that women are rather good at. What were they picking up? Were you concerned?

S. I don't think I was, but that was probably wishful thinking, not wanting my boat to be rocked. Now Lee was working away from home all day, the whole balance of life changed. We had separate lives, his world no longer included me and vice versa. If I went to his workplace, I was there definitely as a visitor. I was increasingly travelling round the region visiting businesses and occasionally we both had work-related meetings in the evening.

R. And amongst that busyness, did you still have time for each other as a couple?

S. We liked to hug, we both needed that.

R. What about intimacy of a closer kind?

S. We didn't get round to sex so often, a quickie in the morning maybe, nothing much else. Lazy sex, in other words, a bit of release for him but generally not very satisfying for either of us.

R. Was that your choice or his?

S. I would probably have done without altogether, but I didn't like refusing. I realised I had gone off sex, with Lee or anyone. I had a dullness within, couldn't be bothered.

R. So when you found the receipt and suspected Lee was involved with someone else, was there an element of relief? Does that sound fair?

S. Probably, I suppose. I was being let off the hook. She was married, happily as far as I knew, so they were unlikely to run off together.

R. That sounds rather odd, a bit cold, and you're not a cold person. I feel there is a lot more to be revealed, but it could be counterproductive to attempt deeper exploration now. It needs to be at a time right for you. In your file, there is the next episode waiting for me, so I suggest we postpone things until next time to see what develops then. What I don't want to do though is to leave you in a kind of limbo. What are your thoughts on the best way forward?

S. This session has been a bit odd for me. Writing the story and then your comments has made me question myself and feel uncomfortable, a bit fuzzy in the head. Your wriggling on a hook analogy has really struck home. Yes, please, let's leave it until next time. A lot more will have been told by then.

Session Three

Hoard | Narrative

THE FOLLOWING WEEK, I WAS working from home, supposedly writing up a report for a client, but I couldn't concentrate. Sitting in the den, I stared at my blank computer screen, dark, opaque. Through the glass came shadows, light and grey, the muted reflection of the window behind me, and the azalea bush beyond. It was strangely hypnotising; I kept peering at it, fascinated, before jerking myself into action. Report writing was put off. I needed to explore the workshop, to see if any hint of Chloe was lurking there. I didn't question whether this would solve anything, action was the imperative, doing something, rather than brooding in front of a screen.

The keys were kept on the windowsill by the back door, including the Yale key to the workshop, attached to a fob of polished elm. On the point of picking it up, I hesitated. Would he know I'd used it? That was immediately followed by realising how ridiculous that sounded. Why shouldn't I go into the workshop, it was part of our joint property. But I felt strongly that each person should have a right to privacy, and their private space should be respected. After all, Lee never intruded on my office space in the den. As a compromise, I fixed the position of the key in my mind and went out to investigate.

Lee had replaced some of the wriggly tin panels in the roof with clear ones. The corrugations made the light coming through muted while holding the gently diffused dust motes in suspension. Did they, I idly wondered, ever settle, or did they hover in an aimless slow dance without end? Dismissing this trivial thought, I stepped in through the door, pulling it to behind me.

I looked around the workshop, at the accoutrements to be expected in a place devoted to serious woodworking. On one side was a collection of bits of machinery – router, saws, drills, planes – anything, in fact, to make procedures easier and quicker. I had a quick look, but nothing appeared untoward. Opposite were the original, solid timber work benches, the genuine workaday article, scarred, stained and scarified, with a time impacted finish that no amount of distressing could ever emulate. Beneath them were chunky wooden drawers with rope pulls for handles. I drew out a couple, and they contained a jumble of old tools and general clutter that looked completely undisturbed. A varying layer of inevitable dust covered all the surfaces in the shed, making any recent activity obvious, but there was no sign. The narrow shelves above were lined with a cluttering of jars and tins harbouring screws, knobs and hinges, mysterious liquids and hardened remnants of paint and varnish.Of course, any evidence could be hidden in plain sight, but his need for secrets probably meant it would be tucked away. But where?

I turned my attention to further back in the building. The space was occupied by items of furniture gathered over the years, plus various lengths of timber. Whole planks were suspended from the ceiling to provide more room below and smaller pieces of all shapes and sizes were piled on the floor or on tables and chests. Passing through a gap between a cupboard and some stacked chairs revealed a cleared space. I'd had no reason to come this far before, as Lee tended to come out to greet me if he was at the back of the building. The waist-high cupboard forming a barrier had some wood piled on the top with an angle poise lamp at one end. Facing it was a captain's style chair with a cushioned seat. This was definitely a cosy nook, but what for? Had Lee got a laptop in here as I first thought? Bending down to look more closely, there was a small gap between pieces of wood, allowing a view through to the doors; a spy hole, an advance warning system for visitors. No wonder he always seemed to know when I entered the workshop.

The cupboard was plain with two doors, but on trying the handle, I found it locked. Curiosity now fully aroused, I looked around for a key, carefully, aware of not disturbing any dust. There were no signs of movement except on the chair and cupboard top, so I risked standing on the chair. Seeing nothing, I stretched up to feel on the top of the nearest stack of wood. My fingers found a key. Clutching it closely in my hand, I stepped off the chair, and on looking closely, I saw the key was the right type and size. The cupboard opened easily, revealing two shelves nearly full of lever arch files. Although the labels were faded, I recognised my handwriting and realised these were discarded files from our previous house. I pulled one out and found it packed with pages taken out of magazines with further files revealing similar contents. They were pictures of women, adults as far as I could tell, engaged in sexual activity with or without accompaniments. I had found Lee's hoard, evidently compiled over a long period, and certainly dating back to well before our move to Scotland. I had not expected this and found it difficult to adjust to this new dimension. These pages represented dozens of magazines, some containing text, which I assumed were stories of an erotic nature, but mainly they were full-colour photos. Some pages bore the name of the magazine, most being the standard fare of top shelves in newsagents, but some from the USA were more explicit. I imagined him taking a sheet or two to work for wanking sessions in the workshop den that Jane had mentioned. What box of fantasies had I opened? Skimming through the files, I realised these were old friends of his, creased, crumbled, foxed by semen stained hands, like a favourite book to be revisited.

The remaining shelf space contained some videocassette cases obviously recycled from the living room collection, a few books, and partly tucked away, a small tub. I eased it out to reveal Body Shop body butter. I stared at it in disbelief. I remembered Lee had been with me when I had bought a three for two offer, and I had assumed they were all in the bathroom cupboard. The hoard had unbalanced me, leaving me slow to realise its purpose. Don't be so naïve, I admonished myself. Wanking cream, of course.

I was aware this wasn't the shock it could have been. I remembered occasions at the previous house, hesitating on the threshold of the workshop before calling his name. Lee would emerge from behind stacked furniture to come forward to meet me. But had there been a hurried tidying away and readjustment before greeting me with apparent innocence? Pornography use wasn't new, because I knew he did it. Many years previously, I'd come home from work early, gone upstairs and found a porn mag on the bed. I didn't move it or say anything, but later it had been removed. Nothing was ever mentioned by either of us.

I felt uneasy about invading his space but before escaping looked at the other items. The videos were not labelled but were probably from late night TV shows. The books were old and worn, obviously second hand. I made a quick flip through one, all text and not overtly pornographic, but enough detail to convince me this was not ordinary fiction. A memory came to the surface, unbidden, of a similar looking book. Several years previously, back in Hereford, I was waiting in the car while Lee was visiting a customer. Not being good at just sitting still, I looked around for something to read. In the glove compartment, I found a book, an old scruffed hardback with no title on the spine. Curious, I opened it at random. It was subtle, but after a few lines, I realised this was no ordinary book. It was quietly sexual, written in the stylised form of the Fanny Hill genre and I recalled a copy doing the rounds at a workplace. I dipped into this book, like a curious puppy, sniffing cautiously at an unknown object before bounding back with a surprised yelp. I replaced it, not really sure of my thoughts, and kept it a secret, never mentioning it to Lee then or later.

By now, enough was enough, as I was starting to feel soiled by handling all this stuff. I knew men needed props, a visual stimulation, while women were far more self-reliant in their pleasuring activities. Even so, I didn't need such a close acquaintance with the details. I put everything back as it was, closed and locked the cupboard and clambered back on the chair to replace the key. Walking slowly back to the house, my mind was churning along with my stomach and drying mouth. It wasn't a case of finding anything particularly excessive, or finding the porn itself. It was the extent of the hoard. He had sneaked in this collection, amassed over a long time, and brought it up to Scotland, presumably travelling in plain sight in the boxes of tools. It was the implicit careful planning, the organisation and deceit of it all.

Back in the kitchen, I suffered a complete blank when I tried to remember the position of the workshop key. Panicking, I forced myself into a degree of calmness and replaced the key in a reasonable approximation of its original place on the windowsill. Next imperative was to make a cup of coffee and get some of my thoughts disentangled. It was obvious the porn activities had existed alongside our marriage for many years, so I was left no further forward regarding the Chloe suspicions, there was no hint of her.

Needing to share these discoveries, I phoned Jane, who suggested we meet in Dalbeattie Forest, as she had an appointment in the town. As it was forecast to be sunny, she thought Beth would really appreciate it too. While we followed a path away from the car park, Beth concentrated on checking out all the smells in the undergrowth. The leaves had gathered under our feet, still holding their turning colours and the rich damp of autumn. I told Jane about the hoard and she was horrified at the content and extent of it.

'If that had been me, I'd have been furious, gathered all the stuff up and dumped it outside. Burnt it there and then. How dare he do all that, it's disgusting.'

I was taken aback by this and thought it a bit over the top. I hadn't reacted that way at the time and didn't feel like it now, but I kept those thoughts to myself.

'The shock was more the amount of stuff and how long it had been going on rather than the content,' I explained, 'because let's face it, porn is what men do, isn't it?

'Yes, but they shouldn't be doing that when they're in a relationship. You've been married a long time, he shouldn't need this stuff.'

'Well, maybe.'

I didn't want to voice the opinion that the opposite could be the case. I continued,

'But I wasn't aware of it impacting on us. I can't get too bothered about the occasional porn mag, as I don't really think it's worth it. I mean, making a fuss about a magazine in the house is not going to stop anyone; it would just make them more secretive. It's the scale of it that's upsetting me. It's comparable to escalating from a few pot plants on the windowsill to a shed full of weed. Let's face it, pornographic images have been around since the beginning, think of those carvings on cave walls from thousands of years ago.'

I started smiling as a humorous angle came to me.

'Just imagine, a prehistoric community. There is a cave decorated with titillating images. A men's cave, where they can disappear for a wank or a communal wank even, who knows. And of course the women would know exactly what was going on and think to themselves, with a knowing smile to their mates, "Goody, that's me left off the hook tonight."'

Jane smiled at the images but then turned serious. I continued,

'We're not going to stop men pleasuring themselves. It's not just a sexual thing, it's a comfort. It's why little boys' hands instinctively seek their crotches in times of uncertainty. Hand in pocket before going into an exam room. It's a comfort zone, a built-in comfort blanket.'

I don't think Jane was completely convinced.

'So what are you going to do about it?'

'Well, there's not much I can do. I still haven't solved what's going on with Chloe. I don't want to rock the boat and just make him retreat into himself, so I think I'll monitor the situation for the time being. However, coming up next week is an event at Druids. It's the anniversary of when the original work was finished in 1900. People are coming down from HQ in Glasgow, while the local people involved in the renovation and all the staff are invited. It would have been nice if Andy and Olive were going, as he did so much on the stonework, but he tends to shy away from functions like this. It means Chloe will be there, so I can watch them both for any further evidence.'

'Sounds good, will you know many people?'

'Not really. I've met Ken, Lee's boss, Chloe of course, and I know others by sight, but admittedly I'm a bit nervous about it. This is Lee in his own territory, part of a team while I'm out on the periphery.'

'Yes, that can be difficult. Sounds like it will be quite an evening though, enjoy it and never mind anything else.'

It would have been hard not to enjoy that evening. Subdued flood lighting flattered the façade of the building and we were greeted with a stunning transformation of the reception hall from the upper gallery along one side to the rafters and beams in the ceiling. Greenery, swathes of flowers, natural fibres and textiles were all woven together, evoking the spirit of the Arts and Crafts movement with stunning effect. The soft lighting gave an ambience of a slower pacing world when there was time to appreciate simple beauty. We joined a table with a group of Lee's colleagues and their partners, including Chloe and her husband. I felt a bit left out as they talked shop and I could only contribute platitudes, clichés or nondescript things. Fortunately, between speeches and a meal, there was little time for talking. At one point, Chloe said some handouts need collecting from the office, and turning to Lee, asked him to help her carry them through. Why ask him? After a few minutes, I wondered what was going on but could hardly go bursting into the office and catch them over a desk. Or they could have disappeared into his workshop in the outbuildings, except that would be pretty risky. This fanciful musing came to an abrupt end by their return to the table, without any sign of covert activity. The only useful snippet I heard was someone mentioning a conference in Edinburgh the following week. Evidently, Lee would be going as the work representative and staying overnight. It was the first I had heard of it but managed to stay quiet, although I brought up the subject on the way home.

'I don't think you told me about that.'

'Oh, I did. It's a conservation conference.'

I left it at that. There was no point in arguing, but I was certain he hadn't mentioned this before.

Hoard | Therapy

Rachael. Well, things have taken a new turn, with the findings in the workshop providing a fresh dimension. Let's concentrate on that and leave Chloe for the moment. You were startled by unearthing this hoard. You were shocked by the extent of it, but not by the fact Lee was using pornography, as you knew he'd used it before. But he had set up part of his workshop for masturbation, no, let's use the colloquial, wanking, sessions. It's the implications of this that seem to be concerning you. Can you say more about that?

Sheena. Yes, it wasn't the wanking itself; it was the creation of a separate world, the construction of a den for his private activities. At the time I found it all rather overwhelming. Here was someone I thought I knew, having another life, another persona even, alongside the everyday 'ordinary' one, right on my doorstep. I didn't expect to find this hoard in our own cupboards; it's far removed from finding the odd porn mag stuffed in a drawer.

R. OK. Let's consider what you found. You were facing the reality of a long-established, extramarital activity, existing in parallel with your marriage, but not, apparently, tainting it; a stable arrangement within set boundaries and no escalation. From the examples you gave, you knew about porn use for some time but seemingly didn't perceive it as a threat. You mention Jane's reaction when you told her. Thinking of other clients I have worked with, I think hers was a common response. They recoil, feel angry and betrayed. And let me emphasise, I am not making any kind of value judgement. You seemed surprised by her reaction though. You took a more rational stance while Jane was more emotional, does that sound fair?

S. Yes, think so. I thought her a bit excessive because... well, it's what men do. Is it really such a big deal? Props to wank to. I'm not comfortable with porn, regard it with some distaste, and there is the enduring paradox of respecting some women and objectifying others.

R. A bit of ambiguity in response, maybe.

S. I suppose I tend to put emotional stuff aside in a crisis, deal with the practicalities first. So appear rational outwardly. Maybe I did that at the time.

R. You seemed to focus on indignation, those things that originally had been yours had been commandeered for his private domain of pleasure.

S. Yes, definitely. These were things that were mine, bought in good faith, and then I see them being used for other purposes, purposes that were very private, that were nothing to do with me, not shared. His private kingdom. I saw that as a contamination.

R. Do you think, possibly, that indignation enabled you to be diverted, away from feeling more emotion about the other elements? Shock numbing your emotional response. Think of how we concentrate on inconsequential aspects in other situations. It's a way to deal with events that we struggle to comprehend.

S. Yes, I see sense in that. Not wanting to face the disbelief and realise it's true. Like belief being suspended. It was certainly a weird experience.

R. And possibly, you were turning to rational answers when giving the reasons for wanking. As you rightly point out, porn use is to do with providing comfort and a sense of security, apart from the obvious physical release. Let's look at Lee's need for porn. He has some degree of dependency on it, but I would hesitate to say addiction. His use does appear to be established within set boundaries; ring-fenced and tucked away. I think I should make clear from the outset that this satisfies a need that has little to do with sex. Sex as the vehicle, not the goal. Lee would be looking to get relief and soothing from whatever anxieties he had at a particular time. He's assimilated porn into his life, which has given him a sense of security. No indication that it has damaged his relationship with you, but that may be proved untrue in further narratives. A false sense of stability, maybe, if there is an escalation to an affair with Chloe. Let's consider this more generally and ask what effect does porn have? Looking at porn magazines releases various chemicals in our bodies, in particular dopamine. This enables us to experience reward and pleasure while directing the brain towards activities that give a reward; a repetitive pattern of pleasure. Now, from what I know so far, I suspect you had little exposure to porn or even much sex education.

S. That's right. Only child and a sheltered childhood meant little opportunity to discover boys and how they worked. However, I remember a time when I was with three or four other little girls, all about six or seven years old. The conversation turned to willies and what they looked like. Most of us expressed some ignorance on this, but one of the girls had superior knowledge, as she had her younger brother with her. She turned to him,

'Get your willie out, you need a wee.'

'Don't want a wee,' protested the squirming victim.

'Yes, you do, get it out, NOW,' she barked.

He gave up and dutifully produced this tiny member for us to gather round and gawk at. It probably scarred him for life and didn't really advance our knowledge other than to prove, once and for all, that we did not possess anything like it.

R. I like that story, poor little chap. He probably ended up in therapy later in life. So, what about later on for you? When did you become aware of pornography in any form?

S. Girly calendars, page three stuff, I suppose. It's the sort of knowledge that gets absorbed by a form of osmosis rather than consciously. There was one lab I worked in with another girl and some young men. They used to joke about wanking and a magazine would appear on the bench sometimes. Hairy pudendas in full colour were not pleasant viewing. The men kept all this between themselves though and there was never any sexist or provocative banter with us girls; we were all equal work mates.

R. That was good, sounds very civilised.

S. Yes, I think I was lucky and naïve. I'm sure a lot of stuff just passed me by, as I would've avoided any blue talk and wouldn't have understood the slang. It wasn't out there in the public domain in the same way it is now. I've never seen a man masturbate. I know some couples do it as a joint enterprise, but I couldn't do that. To me, it's a private thing. It's something that men do, from being young boys; it's nothing abnormal. As I say in the narrative, it is comfort as well as release. Depends on sex drive too, I suppose.

R. Yes, that's true. We have a cultural history of viewing masturbation as dirty, unclean or sinful, although as a society, we are becoming far more tolerant. Some women are shocked and disgusted by it and would try to stop it.

S. Well, it's not going to stop whatever people do. Anyway, what about the female version, or do people pretend that doesn't exist like they used to with lesbians? I first masturbated when I was six, but it was not until my mid-teens that I realised there was a name for it.

R. Yes, we're thinking of the fifties aren't we, when you were six, so it would definitely not be talked about. Still isn't actually, generally speaking, although the majority of women do it.

S. No, certainly not mentioned. Looking back, it was rather amusing. By accident, I had discovered that rubbing a soft toy between my legs gave a very pleasant sensation. I shared this exciting process with a friend, even showing her how to do it. Rosalind must have told her mother, because next thing I know, my mother is asking questions. All children have a finely tuned early warning system for potential problems from parents, and having an unpredictable mother made me more sensitive than most. I instinctively decided that whatever I was asked, no admission would be forthcoming. What exactly had I done? What had I showed Rosalind? received vague or negative replies. It ended in an anticlimax and a command not to do anything like it again, 'anything' unspecified. It taught me to keep quiet.

R. Yes, it was assumed you were doing something wrong and you instinctively kept quiet. I wonder if we can view the male and female versions together. You haven't condemned Lee, defended him actually, and by condoning him, could you be condoning yourself? You both kept quiet to each other and outsiders, which most people would do, and the main motivation is guilt. Should I be doing this? What would people say? No reason for guilt at all, but ours is a society that tends to engender and impose it. Never mind the explicit TV dramas and sex toys being readily available, there is still guilt lurking out there.

S. Don't know about that. But, as well, if these... behaviours... aren't brought out into the open, it means they don't have to be faced. And you don't need to find out if other people do it or if there's something peculiar about you. Asking 'Am I normal?', 'Am I like everyone else?' seems to be quite an obsession nowadays.

R. A lot to reflect on, I think. Let's leave that for now. You have revealed some of your own experiences and I'm curious whether this method of therapy has helped that. Possibly, requiring you to tell your story on paper first has made it easier to talk in these sessions. Could that have happened?

S. Maybe, I wouldn't have come out with all that detail normally, which suggests some loosening up may have happened.

R. Interesting point. Before we finish, let's go back to Chloe, who has been put in abeyance. You didn't find anything in the workshop, and nothing happened at the Druids event, although it sounds a very special occasion.

S. Yes, it was one of those propitious moments, when everything comes together to create a really memorable event. But not taking things forward at all regards Chloe.

R. No, we're no further ahead with Lee and Chloe, if, indeed, there is anything happening. Although there seemed to be some grounds for suspicion and that must have been frustrating for you. I hope the next episode will bring some positive information, as there's another night away planned.

Session Four

Escalation | Narrative

THE TRIP TO EDINBURGH WAS on the following Friday, including an overnight stay. Lee had planned to visit a workshop on the return journey, arriving back early afternoon on the Saturday, upbeat and affectionate. It was a sunny late autumn day, so he happily helped me outside with garden work. The land at the back sloped downhill, but in the past it had been split into two terraced areas separated by a low stone wall. The lower part was mainly grass where previously I had an ark for the hens in the summer. We had decided to plant up one corner with shrubs and perennials, to reduce the grass cutting and provide more interest. On Saturday and Sunday, we continued this project by transplanting and splitting up existing plants. The sun gave sufficient warmth to ignore the crispness of the still air, allowing us to eat a bread and cheese lunch sitting outside. My imagination looked forward to the bare branches covered in green, and the plants pushing their way to the light. Sitting there, looking out over the river estuary, was deceptively alluring, coaxing me into believing that all the porn and suspicions were vague insubstantial imaginings. It provided a break from the pretence of acting normally, keeping up the façade until I had some definitive evidence.

By Tuesday morning, I was resolved to find that evidence.

Again, I suspected the workshop was the best option. I went through the same procedure as before, the cupboard again being locked, but this time, there was no key anywhere. I looked around for other possibilities, before focusing on a white plastic carrier bag sitting on top of a stack of wood. It was folded over, obviously with something in it, the name of a famous supermarket just discernible. I was sure it hadn't been there before, so prodded it with an exploratory finger. There was a hard shape that I recognised as the shower gel bottles we used in the house. What was he doing with this in the workshop? I gently unfolded the bag without actually moving it. Yes, it was shower gel, the lemon scented variety. There was also a small book, which I eased out. It was a pocket diary, dark red, for the current year with the name of a Dumfries company on the front. I didn't know what to expect, possibly a record of his meetings with Chloe. I opened it at random and then stopped, because instead of being the occasional entry, the pages, and I flicked through to check them all, were completely covered in small writing, his writing. What on earth was this? On looking carefully, I saw about eight separate entries on each double page, every one headed by a woman's name followed by age, vital statistics, location, mobile or website and a collection of acronyms that were meaningless to me.

It was one of those situations when time stops, all those clichés coming together about clocks stopping and being frozen to the spot. Well, all that happened. I was fond of detective stories and on occasion, in the Agatha Christie ones, someone walks in on a body lying on the floor of the library. Like me, they can't take it in either. And in a sense, I was looking at a body, the body of my marriage lying there, in the workshop, dead at my feet. Frantically, my imagination was trying to protect me from full comprehension, as the next image to appear was an illustration from a childhood comic. The diminutive humans, open-mouthed, dropped jaws, rooted to the spot, mesmerised by an alien creature slowly rising over the top of a nearby hill. I tried to shake myself back to reality, but it was like a black and white movie, all colour drained and blanched, leaving only the dust beamed light from the roof. I was experiencing a heightened awareness that came entirely from self-produced adrenalin.

I was looking at a list of escorts, escort being the polite term for prostitute; women selling sex, what else do you call them? Supposedly, he had copied all these details off various websites. At the front of the diary was a mixture of telephone numbers and website addresses. I went through the pages from front to back, finding no discernible pattern. The women were from all over the UK, although more concentrated in the North and Scotland. Manchester, for instance, Newcastle, Glasgow and then there was one with an asterisk indicating there was something special about her. 'This is some woman' Lee had written. And there she was, Rosa of Dundee. Mystery, speculations, suspicions all came to an end. From her measurements, she was well endowed, which surprised me, as Lee had always been very appreciative of my more modest attributes. There were more acronyms, but the relevant information was that she offered overnighters (Fridays only).

I got myself together enough to realise I couldn't take the notebook away for leisurely reading; the practical response to crisis was kicking in again. I hurried back to the house to fetch paper and pen and started making notes. I copied out Rosa's details, a few others that looked an accessible distance away and wrote down the names, phone numbers, and website addresses from the front of the diary. I considered other times he had spent the night away, as two escorts were in Manchester and he had been down there a while ago. It dawned on me that he was using these details as a form of pornography, for titilation, as he could not possibly visit them all. I stopped there, was overwhelmed with information. Any further research would have to wait until later.

I returned the diary to the bag and looked at the other contents. There was one more item apart from the shower gel, a rectangular, gold-coloured tin about three or four inches high and ten or so long, like a toffee tin. A particular chocolate selection had come in a cream and brown version with the outside picturing the varieties inside. I remembered we had one of those, so possibly this was it, painted all over in gold paint. I eased it out, not bothered whether he knew it had been moved, as by this time I was like a complete zombie. On opening the hinged lid, I was stunned all over again. Lee had made a lining out of some soft material, and nestling in there were two wine glasses separated by a corkscrew, some condoms tucked down the sides, a strip of paracetemol tablets and a name badge of the sort worn at conferences. Except this one was obviously homemade. Rosa Number I Girlfriend' it declared, with a pin at the back to fix it to... what exactly? With my mind now completely scrambled, my first thought was where the hell does she pin it? At this point, I needed to leave and do the lying down in a darkened room remedy. After replacing everything, I locked up and walked back to the house on autopilot.

I looked for an easy, practical task to convince myself I was still the same person from ten minutes ago. On walking into the kitchen, I instinctively reached for the kettle. Half stumbling, I took it over to the sink and filled it, overfilled it, emptied out the excess, put it on its stand and switched it on. Only functioning at some basic survival level, I got a mug off the hook and reached for the box of teabags. On second thoughts, I needed something to calm me down, and rummaging around in the cupboard, produced a herbal tea, promising peace and relaxation. I dropped the aromatic little bag into the mug and filled up with the now boiling water. As I did so, the string and tag attached to the bag, for fishing it out, slid over the lip of the mug and sunk down into the water. How symbolic, everything else was sliding away too. Sitting at the kitchen table slowly sipping the hot liquid, I gradually wound myself down to normal levels.

Help was needed and I immediately thought of Diane at the medical centre. I phoned, hoping for an early appointment. Having been before seemed to help, as after talking to Diane, the receptionist announced there was a cancellation for eleven o'clock the next day. I gratefully accepted, deciding any work appointments could be sorted out later. Somehow, I got through the evening, making excuses about flu bugs, before going off to bed early with hot chocolate and paracetamol. Next day, I was unclear what to say to Diane, as on my previous visit, the talk had been about my mother. In the event, emotions just overflowed. I walked in and burst out, 'Yesterday was the worst day of my life!' Diane took it all in her stride and calmly heard me out, providing just the impartial, supportive space I needed. She nudged the tissue box and a glass of water towards me and soon I was feeling much calmer. A lot of the emotional baggage had been dumped in that room, albeit temporarily. She gently enquired about my reaction to the escort discoveries, I replied I was shocked, repulsed and disgusted by his behaviour. 'That's good,' she said, 'that's healthy, but I do think Lee needs some serious help.' I agreed with that, but I thought it unlikely he would seek any. I decided to postpone any confrontation with him until I had discovered exactly what he had been doing and the extent of it.

Escalation | Therapy

Rachael. This is a serious escalation, isn't it? I have to admit it came as a bit of a surprise to me. There was certainly something going on, but I thought possibly it was Chloe and went along with your suspicions. Anyway, we can now put a complete stop to that speculation. We have this discovery that left you feeling really shocked. Could we spend a minute or so looking at where that shock was coming from? I fully accept it was a pretty appalling thing to find, but I think we need to unpick it a bit. Up to now, with the pornography business, you seem to be accepting it, not comfortable with it, but accepting and not wanting to challenge him. That has now changed. Can you put into words why it is different?

Sheena. Yes, I wasn't happy with the porn thing, but it'd been going on for a long time. It was like a norm, a set pattern, like a straight line on a machine, and then this escalation was a jump akin to a major blip on a screen monitoring vital signs.

R. Yes, I can understand that, but in what way though?

S. Just... a completely different dimension.

R. Mmm, and by dimension, are we meaning the jump from magazines to internet?

S. Yes, I think so. The photos of women on paper were more manageable, there had been definite boundaries, the pages from magazines were a form of boundary, but with the internet, you have immediately removed all that constraint. That list of sites etc. in the diary, goodness knows what they were. I didn't know at that point, it made for endless opportunities and choices. And because these women were contactable, by phone or text, it made them more real, more tangible, no longer part of a fantasy.

R. I take your point about no boundaries, but are you also saying that arranging real-life meetings is more threatening to a relationship?

S. Very much so. And at the same time, far more exciting, I get that. But it's so much more scary too. What are you getting yourself into when you get involved in this world?

R. Quite. So you see it as a complete escalation. It's obvious by the way you describe things that you are in a state of shock. I find it interesting that you use the image of a body on the library floor, because in a sense, in several senses, we're talking about loss. You've lost a rather comfortable view of pornography, you had convinced yourself that actually this is not too much of a threat, you can cope with it, but you can't with this. This is something utterly different, so you've lost the bit of comfort you had. And you've lost the... well, you tell me, what other losses do you think are involved here?

S. Loss of the man I thought I knew. I just didn't think... I didn't think he would do that, it never occurred to me. I had lost him to another world and along with that, of course, is a massive lost of trust.

R. Yes, trust, the big one. We haven't really mentioned it before, have we, but it has been an underlying theme, now pushing through to the forefront. Obviously, if Lee had been having an affair, there would've been trust issues. As we didn't know, we didn't face head-on the fact that trust had been broken. Now we do have loss of trust, loss of perception. Was there anything not lost?

S. Well, some things weren't lost. We used to have, and in many respects still had, a very deep friendship based on sharing experiences over the years. That forms a bond of memories that cannot be actually broken. It is the bond of lovers, the bond of the exclusive pleasure in another's body that is broken, completely and irretrievably, as soon as infidelity takes place. That is a major loss. And... and I am having to query myself, ask what am I doing here? How responsible am I? What does this say about me? Does it mean I am basically a crap person that he can treat me like this? There was a loss of confidence. Do I lose my identity? I am no longer a loved partner but spurned... not sure I want to go there right now. I think this has the potential for being very upsetting.

R. Yes, and we're not going to go there at the moment. You are not in the right place for any in-depth exploration, so let's just concentrate on you and connect with how you were feeling at the time.

S. I remember feeling very fragile, lurching around, not quite sure what I was doing, fuzzy-headed.

R. Your life had just taken a seismic shift. The perception of your husband and the trust you had in him had been lost, so we could, in a sense, treat what happened as a form of bereavement. What you were feeling, experiencing, are very similar to what people go through when someone close to them physically dies, bereavement in the conventional sense. Can you relate to that view at all?

S. Mmm, I don't... I don't think I would have described it like that, I wouldn't have made that connection. But I suppose when someone close to you dies, the whole world turns upside down, nothing's the same, can never be the same, so in that sense, yes, I can see there are similarities. How does that help though?

R. It helps in the sense that we can have some understanding of what you needed then, in the process of grieving, what would have been helpful for you. And what is needed now, still, because the grieving process can last for years, a lifetime sometimes. In a conventional bereavement, if there is such a thing, you go through a period of shock and disbelief. You don't know where you are, what's happening, you are certainly not in a position to start reasoning and seeking answers. Usually, the best thing that can happen is for you to have somebody around who you can just talk to, say whatever you want to, blurt it all out and get the pressure down. And this counsellor, Diane, whether or not she articulated a comparison to bereavement doesn't really matter, because in effect, that's what she was doing. She was letting you talk, being objective, in confidence. In the narrative, you went to see her that once. Did you see her other times after that?

S. Yes, I did, two or three times, I think, and really it was the same each time. As you said, it was her being supportive. She just let me say what I wanted, I didn't really have a rant about him, but I was horribly hurt. I didn't get angry, just asked why did he do it? Why? Why? But I didn't address that.

R. It wouldn't have been appropriate then, too much raw pain and bewilderment. I think maybe we take a similar approach here, because even if it was several years ago, writing about it will have brought back how you felt in that workshop.

S. Absolutely, those feelings are being brought back, coming through to the present. I found that piece very difficult to write, mentally draining and pulling me down physically. It did take me right back to how it felt then, making it all very real again. I didn't know what was going to happen. So I think I would like some reflecting space.

R. Of course. You need the same type of space you needed at the time, because in a sense, this is a further stage in the loss process. Before we finish, can I just ask... Obviously, the Chloe issue was put completely out the window, but did you feel that as a relief?

S. I don't think I did actually, because in some ways, I would've preferred it to be Chloe, it would've been more straightforward. I did question whether I'd been a complete idiot suspecting her, but actually no, there was something happening; I just had the wrong end of the stick basically. She became an irrelevance. Rachael... we have some time left, haven't we?

R. Yes, we have. I just thought you may like to finish early today.

S. Yes, appreciate that, but something has come up I should like to talk to you about. As I said, writing the narratives has brought back all the emotions felt at the time, but also brought up memories I was unaware of while writing. They emerged after we started going over things in more depth. Last week, out of nowhere, one particular episode came back, breaking through the surface with no warning. I've been trying to identify specific events that could have triggered Lee's escalation. This particular memory may have been one of them, even though it was a few years before the breakup. It was all to do with a boat.

R. I'm intrigued. Please tell and take whatever time you need.

S. As I have described earlier, we were living on a river estuary leading out to the Solway Firth, so inevitably at low tide, banks of glistering mud emerged with a deep water channel down the middle. There were some small sailing cruisers moored in the river; all with twin keels so they could sit on the mud between tides and a few dinghies on trailers in a parking area. I had sailed a bit when younger and Lee was interested in a general sort of way, so we often wandered down to watch any boat activity. In the storage yard, tucked away at the back, was an elderly wooden sailing dinghy about twelve feet long of the clinker build immortalised by Arthur Ransome in *Swallows and Amazons*. As an AR fan, I was immediately drawn to this little boat and, of course, Lee was delighted there was at least one 'proper boat', as he put it. She was called *Marie* and looked a bit forlorn, as though she had been left to gently doze in the hope that one day she would again feel water under her keel.

R. Sounds like love at first sight. I know exactly the sort of boat you mean and they do have a certain charm while being very pleasing to the eye. So what happened?

S. We knew George, one of the cruiser owners, so we asked him about *Marie*. He explained that the previous year, the boat had been damaged on one side of the bows after hitting a rock. Paul, the owner, had repaired her before putting her up for sale but without success. Paul worked away during the week, but a couple of Sundays later, we were talking boats with him over a pint or two in the pub. He was pleased we wanted to take *Marie* on as a winter project and offered to let us have various bits of gear that went with the boat. She came with a road trailer and the figure he asked for her seemed very reasonable. We didn't need a discussion and a couple of weeks later, *Marie* was sitting on her trailer outside Lee's workshop.

We spent that winter stripping the paint off the hull and replacing it with layers of varnish. It was obvious where a new plank had been fitted, but it looked sound. We overhauled all the rigging, varnished the mast and spars and bought a small outboard motor for her. I saw the boat as symbolic. We were no longer home-based, sharing a space, so the boat restoration was a couple enterprise, a way of working together.

Many winter evenings were spent musing and dreaming of future adventures. Lee was by far the more practical one, so had no fears about handling the boat under engine or oars. I knew more of the sailing side, so between us we thought we could manage, and George had offered some lessons once we were on the water.

R. Mmm. Listening to you, I am hearing a lot of emotional energy being invested by both of you in this little boat. It is interesting you viewed it as symbolic and I wonder if this was a way to reignite your couple relationship. Possibly unconsciously, you were beginning to realise you were slowly drifting away from each other. Maybe that's why you've suppressed the memory. Just a thought, but please go on.

S. OK, so in the spring, we took *Marie* down to the slipway and launched her into her natural habitat. We knew she would take up water for a while, as wooden boats dry out if left on shore for a long period. We resigned ourselves to bailing out for a few days before choosing a calm day and high tide to try a short voyage using the outboard rather than the sails. This turned out to be fortuitous. We left the floorboards up to make baling easier if it became necessary. Some water crept in, as expected, but after a while, I realised I was losing the baling game and the water was coming over my feet. On looking up, I found Lee eyeing the water with apprehension, and by instant, tacit agreement, we turned round and headed back. We hauled her out on her trailer, but the water stayed inside, so no obvious leaks. George had been watching us and came over to help. He couldn't come up with an answer but suggested we ask a marine surveyor, who was visiting the following week.

Luckily, the surveyor welcomed the opportunity to look at a wooden boat, albeit a little one. He went over her very carefully and then explained that the repair had been botched. As well as the plank, a rib had been replaced but hadn't been fitted properly into the keel, thus allowing abnormal movement of the adjacent planks. In other words, essential rigidity had been lost.
Sitting at the pontoon would have been fine, but any forward motion would allow water to come into the boat. Paul refused

to take responsibility, even though he had done the repair and must have known he had botched it. We hadn't paid much for her but, even so, didn't feel we should have to pay for the repairs. Relations deteriorated rapidly so that in the end, we took him to the Small Claims Court and he settled the claim just before the payment deadline. We were furious at him that we had been duped and furious at ourselves that we had been taken for fools. He had obviously taken advantage of our boat ignorance and it all left a nasty taste.

Lee's confidence took a profound knock, particularly as it involved wood, his speciality. He took it very personally and resisted any attempts by me to reason that he was in no way to blame, as he was not a boat builder. He refused any discussion, although I tended to be more philosophical about the situation. Much to our relief, a local wooden boat specialist agreed to take her. I am left wondering if this was a major contributor to Lee's lack of confidence and his need to find comfort for himself. It was very significant for him and the fact that I buried the experience so deeply implies it was significant to me too. Maybe I didn't want to face up to being taken for an idiot. I just buried it, until now. But was it sowing the seeds for Lee's escalation?

R. What a sad story. I really feel for both of you. Lee's a proud person, isn't he? I think that comes through in your narratives, so he would've taken it all particularly hard. And been very hard on himself, as you indicate. You suggest the boat was a way of strengthening your couple relationship, a way which had now failed, so was it an omen for the future? Did it indeed sow the seeds for Lee's escalation? I certainly think it is likely, but possibly we will learn more in the following narratives.

Session Five

Revelations | Narrative

DESPITE HAVING MUCH TO DO investigating escort sites, I couldn't face it just yet. I slowed down, right down, rather like when you have been involved in running an event. You've been racing around, full of activity, and then it's all over, everyone gone, everything cleared away. Like flopping down on a giant cushion, physically and mentally drained. I knew what had to be done, enter the murky sinkhole of those websites; a world not unknown but not experienced. I had to face reality, but my tectonic plates needed to settle back to an approximation of their original position.

There was other work to do and clients to see. They didn't want a miserable woman, spurned and dejected, bringing her contagion into the workplace. They needed a positive force providing answers, like the performer bouncing on to the stage, hitting the ground running. Slinking on halfheartedly was not what the audience was paying for. I imagine many people, when melancholia creeps in, opt for upbeat cheerfulness in their music choices; like Inspector Morse and his soaring operatics. I tended to indulge the melancholia, hoping that by intensifying, it would burn itself out. I had a fair bit of travelling to do, so loaded up the CD stack in the car boot with suitable discs.

I had long been a fan of the country singer and songwriter Kris Kristofferson, and his pessimistic breaking up and leaving themes reflected my downbeat state. Other days, I played the echoing clarity of Annie Lennox's 'Pavement Cracks' at high volume, thumping the steering wheel in time to the bass notes. Beth, lying on the front seat, shifted around with a protest grunt at the noise before settling back with a resigned sigh. 'I Don't Know You Anymore', from James Grant, the Scottish singer/songwriter, proved to be too doleful, and then there was John Martyn, a favourite of both of us, bringing back happier times travelling to his concerts in Glasgow. For a few days, I needed that musical escape while juggling the wish to start investigating with the wish to slink away and ignore it all.

Of course, in the end, curiosity won, that need to know. I carried a cup of coffee through to the den to study the notes I'd made. Where to begin? Random thoughts had the freedom to speak but were drawn to that one name, Rosa. I began with a general website offering escorts of various orientations and locations; commodity marketing akin to car selling sites. Under location, I tapped in 'Dundee' and there she was, Luscious Rosa. Clicking on her website link revealed her in all her lusciousness. She was a large woman and obviously proud of it, presented as a selling point. There was a photo of her, perched on the front edge of a chair, propped up by her arms, legs wide apart and balancing on high heels. A bit ridiculous, as she was wearing a basque-type garment reaching down to cover her pudenda, lacy top black stockings, elbow-length white gloves and a black full-face mask. She exemplified the comic element of a Tom Sharpe character, without the latex, but this was all utterly serious. The blurb said 'If your (sic) a big boob lover then I'm the girl for you. All natural.'

Her other attributes were as noted in Lee's diary, including being 'shaved for your pleasure' and 'big, blue ringed tits'. With the help of Ask Jeeves, I discovered the meaning of the synonyms quoted here and on other entries, OWO meant oral without condom, A was anal and CiM was cum in mouth. Intriguingly, she had a guestbook where clients could make their comments, like a Trip Advisor for escorts. I was taken aback to find that Lee of Dumfries had a post. 'Rosa has the most delightful pale clear skin and curves in all the right places. Treat her well and you will reap the reward. Treat her well anyway; she deserves no less.' What a load of pretentious rubbish, was my first reaction. Other client comments included 'C'mon boys she is worth every penny', 'Had a very nice time', 'Would highly recommend this lady for an enjoyable time', etc. Snooping on a secret masculine world felt profoundly odd, bringing an eerie skin tingling. I went off for more coffee, feeling chilled and a bit shaky after venturing into this alien territory.

I turned to the list of phone numbers I'd found in the front of the diary. Except for two in Carlisle, they were all mobiles, giving no idea of location. Phoning them was quickly dismissed, being obviously female with no acting talent for disguise. I didn't think Jane would be comfortable doing it, and asking a male friend was also dismissed. Eventually, the obvious answer came – use a private detective; the species beloved of mystery novels. I consulted the yellow pages and found one, far enough away that they wouldn't know either of us. A pleasant male voice answered the phone.

'I was wondering if you could help, please, with getting some information about my husband. Do you do that sort of thing?'

'Possibly, it depends what sort of information. Let me say first that I'm an ex-policeman. I usually do missing persons searches or background information on prospective staff for employers. I don't do anything illegal.'

'Right. Well, I don't think this is illegal. My husband has been seeing escorts, prostitutes, in various parts of the country. I have found a list of phone numbers that I would like to check out, but I can't really phone them myself.'

After a pause, 'Are you saying you would like me to phone these numbers and pose as a punter?'

'Yes, that's right.'

He chuckles.

'Well, not sure what my wife will say and this is certainly a first for me. What exactly do you want to know?'

'Where they operate. I know he sees one in Dundee, but I would like to know if there're any local ones, such as in Dumfries, or if they come to Dumfries, and is it incall or outcall.'

'Outcall being meeting in a hotel you mean?'

'Yes, and incall is when they have a flat or somewhere to take clients.'

'Ok, I'll have a go. See how I get on. Normally there would be a contract, but it doesn't sound as though it should take very long. You're not expecting me to arrange a meeting, are you?' He laughs, 'Not going to do that.'

'No, don't worry. You don't need the full experience. Can you give me any idea of cost?'

I arranged to send him a cheque and the telephone numbers. About a week later, he phoned back.

'Well, that was a new experience, interesting. One Carlisle number was for a club disguised as a brothel, reading between the lines. It was an Asian-sounding woman who answered the phone and offered me girls from Thailand, with a new selection coming shortly. There was no answer from the other Carlisle number. The escort called Diz is in Dumfries, near the centre with her own place, and she sounded local to me. One of the others was not in

Dumfries and didn't go there herself but knew someone who did. Another one came to Dumfries a few times a month according to demand. She had premises and you could book an appointment. She seemed to be part of an organised group, as I gathered there was more than one woman involved, took it in turns maybe. An interesting job, thank you for giving me an insight into the escort world.'

I thanked him, as that seemed useful information as far as it went, but the most satisfying part was being proactive.

Other thoughts began to emerge, not particularly welcome ones. I was left with that niggling question coming back, the one I had swept aside while pretending the suspected affair with Chloe didn't matter. I'd been kidding myself; of course it mattered. It had prevented me from addressing the fundamental question. Why had I gone off sex when, in one form or another, it had always been important? Does libido die suddenly or does it creep quietly away to die slowly in a corner? Sex mattered because to me it was an integral part of affection and closeness. That aspect was important, as I had had few cuddles or a physical displays of affection from my parents. I don't remember them showing much affection to each other either.

I needed to trace this through from the beginning. My mother and I lived with her parents while my father was abroad in the years following the last world war. Evidently, a habit was established of sitting on my grandfather's knee while he read his newspaper. As I pointed to the words, asking what they were, he would patiently teach me, so I could read long before starting school. His arm would be round me for support, giving affectionate contact, the warmth of closeness that didn't come from anyone else. Then tragedy struck, as he died just after my fifth birthday, leaving no conscious memory of him. It's a complete wipeout but left a legacy of associating affection and comfort with a male person. Starting with a young cousin, there was always a supportive male figure in my life, catching me before I fall, as the country songs say. It might've been a boyfriend, a lover or simply a good friend, but someone was always there.

Eventually, in my late teens, I was involved with an older man, twenty-seven or so. The inevitable happened, we had sex, and I lost my virginity. Why lost? As if it's something you unwittingly leave behind you. Should you not be giving rather than losing, as it can never be regained. He was considerate, and I was compliant, so nothing to complain about, but the earth didn't move. I was very immature and naïve, and this being the early sixties, information was not readily available. Despite that, I was aware that there should be something a bit more. Some women probably tolerate a lacklustre performance for the sake of having marriage and children, but I wasn't looking for either of those. I wanted a bit more from the sex side of things.

A while after my 'loss', I started a new job and got a regular lift home with a work colleague, again several years older. He had a reputation for keeping his brain between his legs, as a work mate put it. The naughty boy image is an attractive one and he was attracted to me. The upshot was we would sit up the road from my parents' house, in his Austin Somerset, to consider how to further my sex education. Neither of us wanted the girlfriend/ boyfriend thing yet, so after some discussion, he suggested he could be of help, leading to an arrangement where every so often we diverted to his flat on the way home.

The main event in my learning was with another man about nine or ten years older. There was an intense physical attraction to him on first meeting, the clichéd, sizzling current crossing the room, and he felt the same. There were no violins, flowers and dreaminess, no sweet nothings. This was sexual attraction, pure and simple. Although the relationship developed more broadly to encompass social outings, concerts and dinners, it was never very affectionate. It was never conventional 'going out together'. In fact, he treated me pretty badly overall, as it was very much an on/off affair, making him, in old-fashioned parlance, a cad. He would break it off, then come back, and of course, I couldn't resist. The first time it happened, I was devastated, with frighteningly intense feelings. Thankfully, I recovered sufficiently to think, 'sod him' and found someone else closer to my own age. The pattern was repeated over several years.

For the purposes of this narrative, the important point is that he was seriously good at sex. At least, that's my subjective judgement. I suppose it's more accurate to say we were compatible in our tastes and appetites. Not much love about it, but we both enjoyed the physical side, suggesting an equality in the giving of pleasure. In reality, there was little equality, although he played the power games at a deceptively low level. It must have been around this time I learned that valuable lesson: do not confuse lust with love; they can be mutually exclusive. We tended to go to his flat, the upper floor of an old coach house in the grounds of a private mansion, giving magnificent views of the river and surrounded by acres of woodland. The coach house, reached by a separate track and not overlooked, provided an idyllic location; a green grotto with a view of water. At some point, it had been used as a studio and the windows had been enlarged, filling the living space with light, tinged with green from the surrounding trees.

The first coupling – 'lovemaking' is inaccurate – had long-term repercussions, as it was important for all the wrong reasons. He knew I was attracted to him, so couldn't understand why I was reluctant and holding back, probably assuming I was teasing.

I did desire him, absolutely no doubt about that, achingly so, but I didn't want it hurried. I needed it slower and gentle and let's face it, more idealistic. This was the sixties, the age of love, I was looking for the flowery bit but couldn't articulate my objections. I didn't know how to say what I wanted without sounding stupid and immature. He was not rough at all but quietly insistent. Eventually, I just gave in, meaning he had sex with me when I wasn't really willing, leaving psychological consequences.

That first experience left me feeling unsettled, distrustful, as if he had put up a barrier preventing me from fully relaxing. Nevertheless, the relationship continued, the chemistry was too strong. Subsequent lovemaking was very different from the first time, although I never had a full orgasm with him. I got very close but never quite there, never over the edge, just a series of mini ones along the way, multiple minis as it were. The Cad was not happy about this, treated it as a challenge, although eventually became resigned. I seemed to be holding myself back as a protection and was sufficiently curious to ask a doctor friend for his thoughts. He immediately scoffed, 'Of course you're not frigid. He's the problem, not you,' which was reassuring to hear. I didn't have the same problem with subsequent men, though I admit to occasionally embellishing my response for effect and in appreciation of my partner's efforts.

But why was he so good? The Cad left me with a legacy of setting a standard; I owe him that at least. There were no fancy positions or manoeuvres, as it was conventional; missionary with variations plus mild flirting with oral. Part of it was practising sustained foreplay at a distance, providing a long buildup of seduction. He was fond of dining out and we would work our way through the local entries in the latest *Good Food Guide*. The ambience in those eateries plus the marvellous food and wine remain a vivid memory. A relaxed form of wooing that has a long history of success. Back at home for intermediate foreplay, we would sit by candlelight listening to music, usually baroque, or occasionally Dylan, sipping a glass of wine. Again, a time honoured technique. Finally, we would reach the close foreplay stage when we were lying in bed side by side with candlelight and possibly a slow rendering of Mozart's clarinet quintet, as featured in Agnès Varda's film *Le Bonheur*. I suspect that was a deliberate choice because it was like a film set, with careful attention to detail, like part of a coordinated stage.

I honestly think he fancied himself as a director of one of the foreign art films we used to go to. These were nothing like as explicit as the average TV drama now, just artistic nudity without full-frontals. Slow and sensuous, they were erotic in the sense of being tantalisingly beautiful films, by the leading directors of the day such as Godard, Antonioni and Varda. Sex as an art form, no raunchy stuff, no crude language, just subtle music and lighting, all about anticipation and taking time. Maybe he imagined looking down on himself, directing his own performance, a studied conductor. The effect was helped by us being very similar physically; tall, slim, long legs providing a harmonious collage of entwined limbs. The film directors would have loved us.

We both had slender sensitive fingers and I learned the value of gentle stroking, with subtle changes in pressure, the sensuous feathering touch at which we both excelled. Slowly roaming all over our bodies until the skin was singing while avoiding the sexual bits. I preferred this, as outside fumblings and fingerings had little effect; the most sensitive area being around and just inside the entrance of my vagina. I had no idea at that time the anatomical significance of this. It was only much later that I questioned what was happening, after reading that a vaginal orgasm wasn't possible due to insufficient nerve endings in that area. I knew what worked, accepted it and let it be. For me, penetration was very important; having someone inside purely for pleasure is the most intimate and close you can get.

When eventually the Cad was inside me, he could continue for an impressively long time, varying speed, slight changes in angles, moving in and moving out. He had control at virtuoso level, so I assumed he had trained himself to emulate the art film characters. There were occasions when we stayed in bed all weekend, only getting up to pad through to the kitchen for coffee, bread and cheese. Looking back after all these years, I realise I have donned rose-tinted spectacles so rosy bright they're dazzling. There was lovemaking but no love words. I have glossed over the not so good bits, realising he was very self-indulgent, with me being one of the indulgences. He was fastidious about food, particularly coffee. At that time, proper coffee came ready ground, in Lyons green tins. The Cad sourced whole beans, Blue Mountain for instance, from specialist shops, ground them at home and made coffee in a large pot. I loved the quality, the aesthetics of it all, without realising how pretentious and precious he really was. Back then, I just enjoyed it without a critical eye, as there was a lot of magic mixed in with the hurt and disappointments. He set the sexual standard that all other men were judged by and, to be honest, no one else matched him until I met Lee.

Lee had a natural talent, which compensated for his lack of experience, as I was older by nine years. We had the ideal combination of best friends, pals, lovers and partners. Finally, I had the supporting male and the sexual role in the same person, making for a fuller relationship and a great source of pleasure. Together we followed a similar sexual philosophy and style to the Cad legacy, although living together required adjustments. We made time for dedicated lengthy sessions, teasing and laughter ending with a synchronised finish; my legs waving in the air from sheer joy. A deep shared pleasure. So what happened? How and where did we lose that harmony?

Revelations | Therapy

Rachael. This narrative has a mixture of themes, suggesting we have reached a significant point, a waymark in the process as a whole. Let's just recap. We began with the aim of understanding your marital breakdown. You have given some background to your life with Lee, interspersed with the story of a suspected affair and the discoveries of pornography use and escorts. Interwoven with all that are your reactions to Lee's behaviour. This time, you explore the escort details, including the input of a detective. Must admit I liked that bit. Not the sort of thing you can ask a friend to do and certainly not a male friend. It would take an enormous amount of trust. Following on, there's discomfort reading the comments on Rosa's website. It was very much a secret male world, secret from women friends and partners at least. I can appreciate how that was uncomfortable. It might be worth pointing out that the whole escort/prostitute world has its own hierarchy, ranging from street corner soliciting through to an extremely expensive top of the range service. The world you are looking at here is somewhere near the middle of this, a certain veneer of respectability coming from having their own websites. Despite that, this is paid-for sex, pure and simple, with the buyer in ultimate control.

Sheena. Yes, I can see that. The comments were not derogatory or abusive, they were complimentary even, although leaving no doubt concerning the overall attitude; this woman is for male entertainment.

R. That's right. You then start asking questions about yourself. The reason you lost interest in sex has been lurking in the background. Up to now, I think we've been skittering around the subject, allowing it to be pushed back by other events. We are getting closer to finding answers. Does that sound fair?

S. Yes, I think it does. I sensed something was different when I wrote this piece, though I'm not sure what. As if I'd reached the top of a slope and was now edging my way down the other side, seeing a clearer path. Or, to use another metaphor, the knots were starting to unravel, but I had to go on. I couldn't retie them.

R. That's good. The process has started, you're seeking answers. Nudging by the therapist is all very well, and necessary sometimes, but it's likely to be a more rewarding process if the questioning is begun voluntarily. Part of the answer lies in the historical sex information, as that establishes its importance for you. Sex is an activity that gives you the closest physical contact to another person.

S. Looking back, I was aware that any contact, a hug or holding hands, was a way to connect at some level. Because it was usually with men, I tended to associate the contact with sex, in the wider sense. It took me a long time to accept and rejoice in the touching of friendship.

R. Yes, and being a loner and preferring male company, you were probably reluctant to be close to any girls. Obviously, hugs are not necessarily sexual and I am glad you made that distinction. Early on, your reasoning was, hugs meant male and male meant sex in some guise.

S. I think that's true. I had girl friends but don't remember discussing intimate details with them. I suppose, in a way, I viewed sex or mild sexual contact as a form of nurturing.

R. Yes, it can be viewed that way. You were good at sex, which gave you confidence. It was an activity, essentially yours, without a mother standing offstage calling, 'Do you really think you're any good as a lover?' This was private territory, safe from her. Sex can be symbolic, so understanding its role could lead to understanding the broader picture.

S. Hmm, as you were talking, I felt myself agreeing, some light coming in and... relief, I think. That understanding is happening. Will need some reflecting time, but that's what it's all about, isn't it?

R. Very much so and we have started the process. Let's turn back to the narrative and this rather enchanting picture of a retreat in the woods. You say it was like an art film, and that's how it reads, with you a simpatico partner on a stage set of his designing, but not necessarily, I would suggest, valued for yourself. I confess I did listen to Mozart's clarinet quintet, played with a slow sensuousness that felt absolutely right. Although, for all those honeyed notes, the apparent idyll on the surface had unsettling undercurrents, echoing the darker themes that

Varda wove through *Le Bonheur*. You were reluctant in that first sexual encounter, you 'gave in', which does not imply willingness. It reads as if you blamed yourself for not being able to express how you felt. Subsequently you proved an enthusiastic playmate, despite the relationship being erratic and unpredictable. I feel a lack of simple kindness about all this, when being kind is vital to successful relationships. You had a strong attraction to this man, but were you hoping for a permanent relationship?

S. At the time, I did wonder, but if I'm honest, I recognised the thrill of the chase. The uncertainty and the allure of the unobtainable had its own attraction.

R. I wonder if you would've gone through with a marriage. Something vital could've been lost when making a commitment, which is another way of saying there was insufficient substance to sustain a marriage. You mentioned turning to other partners when the Cad broke it off, yet again. How did you manage that? Was there a lot of juggling?

S. Yes, it could get tricky. You can't dance the last dance with two people! Overlapped sometimes for a while. It was all pretty disastrous and I escaped in the end by moving to another part of the country.

R. That was a wise move, because there appeared little hope of breaking that toxic situation. There's a lot here about your sexual response, justifying an excursion into the realms of sex therapy. To put things in perspective, female sexual responses vary widely between individuals and the reason lies, partly, with anatomy. Some years ago, one of the Sunday colour supplements had a two-page spread showing rows of passport-size photos of female genitalia. Nothing pornographic about it, strictly medical images, displaying the astonishing variation in size, shape, position and colour. For instance, the most sensitive part, the clitoris, can be very close to the vaginal entrance or some distance away. It takes little imagination to realise that a range of techniques may be required to give the most sensation when individuals vary so much. Furthermore, the visible structures are only part of the story, as the clitoris extends inwards and can be inside the entrance of the vagina or within the adjacent wall. If the so-called G spot is regarded as part of the clitoris, rather than a separate entity, it explains why not all women have one. Although strictly speaking the vaginal orgasm may be a myth, as you have mentioned, there can be great sensitivity near the entrance. The group with this type of anatomy may find penetration critical for orgasm while others with different characteristics find it less relevant. There are no rights or wrongs, no normal, just difference, as everyone has to adapt to their own bodies. Unfortunately, many men assume women are all the same, and women are reticent about voicing their preferences. Getting it right is the most difficult balancing act of all human interaction.

Right, that's the theory diversion over.

S. Yes, thank you for that. Explains a lot.

R. To return to the Lee question, you did make a commitment to him. Am I right in assuming there were no infidelities on your part?

S. No, never felt any temptation sexually, even though we'd been married a long time before I lost interest. It was a general loss though, not just with him. I wasn't on the lookout for a new flirtation.

R. You described the outfit Rosa wore on her website. Many couples enjoy dressing up, to introduce some variety and innocent fun in their sex lives. There is no suggestion of anything like this in your narratives. Maybe you were seeking other kinds of change but not in your sex life.

S. No, I would have been uncomfortable doing that, self-conscious, as not my natural habitat. Stupid really, because given a gentle introduction, I may have ended up enjoying it.

R. Overall, I think sex was acting as a barometer, the medium through which the health of your relationship could be measured, but was it the cause? Highly unlikely, I would have thought. It's as though you felt malaise, tired of the status quo. I think we are talking about change here, the need for change on your part and some actions that acted as a catalyst to draw you apart. Too big a subject to start here today. The next narrative may help us, but I am aware that we are lacking more background information on Lee, as I think that could hold some clues for our understanding. Does that sound like a way forward?

S. Yes, I can give more on Lee next time.

Session Six

Confrontation | Narrative

I MET JANE FOR COFFEE to update her, including the detective's role. She burst out laughing, earning some glances from people at the nearby table.

'I can't believe you did that.'

'Not sure I do either, but it was the obvious way to go.'

'For you maybe, I don't think I would've even thought of it.'

'But I wanted to find out.'

Jane took some contemplative sips of her coffee, obviously wondering about something.

'Do you... do you really think he is seeing women, locally?'

'There's one in Dumfries, I have the phone number. If you think about it, he's going to Dundee once a month, he may need a lunchtime quickie. I mean, the mind boggles a bit, doesn't it?'

'Yes, very. Sorry, having difficulty getting my head around this. I suppose he could arrange for one of these girls to visit Dumfries.'

'Hmm, well, what I am going to do is look through his bank and credit card statements. We each have a box file for our private stuff and would usually respect that, but it's no longer usual.'

'Yes, very much no longer. What did you say it cost to visit this Rosa woman, £300 a night?'

'Yes, there's the room and travel, so fuel and presumably a meal, and of course the bottle of wine to justify the corkscrew and glasses.'

I paused. We looked at each other, torn between laughter and incredulity at the bizarre situation. Jane continued,

'It could add up to nearly £400. Where is the money coming from? It's that old saying, isn't it, follow the money.'

'Exactly, on looking through the other sites, Rosa was pretty reasonable. If he had used someone in Glasgow, he could be paying around £1000 or more.'

'This all seems to be taking on a life of its own. Surely at some point, you'll have to confront him?'

'Yes, I realise that, but not ready just yet. I need to find out more, because once I've confronted him, a lot of this stuff might not be available. I'm going to my mother's next week for the pre-Christmas visit, which could be his last chance for a night away, not that he knows that. A day, no, two days, after I get back, I'll confront him.'

That was pronounced in more definite tones than I actually felt.

'Ok, so does that set a date?'

'Yes, think it does.'

I had made a decision, out loud, with a witness, whom I am sure would hold me to it. Relief swept over me, the snooping was coming to an end.

Back at home, a new worry emerged. How was I going to manage the confrontation? The decision to do it was one thing, but the exact mechanics were a different proposition altogether. Anyway, I needn't face that just yet. I started work on my investigations, conscious that time was now limited. I recalled the mantra from the crime novels I enjoyed; motive, means and opportunity.

I knew the motive but now needed to track the other two. Previously, I'd never rummaged about in his private papers and assumed he had not in mine, although both of us could have done; all the information being readily available. There had been an unspoken agreement to respect each other's privacy. Women are their own worst enemies in many ways, because once doubt sets in, once a suspicion gets implanted, it grows until evidence has to be found, by fair means or foul. All the niceties of respecting privacy go out the window in one job lot. Trust has been damaged, the bond ruptured along a tattered length; no rules remain. The workshop stuff was different; this was bringing his deception into the house, a shared domain. This was a final breach of trust.

Sitting in the den, I took out the credit card statements, clipped together neatly in date order. Immediately, my mind went blank, the figures blurring with no rhyme or reason. Then I remembered the voucher I had seen was in September, so I selected that statement and, true enough, there it was, £49, plus the booking Jane had phoned about. There were no further entries, although a quick look at the bank statements confirmed he was probably paying by cash. I found three withdrawals of £100, which tied in with Rosa's fee, or whatever it was called, but I needed a more organised approach. In order to see a clear pattern, spreadsheets were the obvious choice to my logical type of mind, as I used them extensively at work. It struck me then that finding patterns may be a useful way to starting the conversation on confrontration day, or C day, as I'd begun to call it. This was information readily available, limiting the amount of snooping I would have to reveal.

I began with columns for month, date and cash withdrawn. After starting with September, I realised the need to look further back, to get an idea of a 'normal' month. I turned to considering what else was happening in our joint lives that may have needed cash. My diary recorded work appointments but also noted meals and events. An additional column for these proved useful, as I could eliminate some of the purchases straight away. Compiling all that left my brain in furred up mode. I'd never been particularly stressed by creating spreadsheets before, but now I was recording my husband's private activities, his clandestine life of deceit. My forensic self was starting to crumble. I saved the sheets into an innocent-sounding file, although my computer was password protected, as it held client stuff.

I had found the means, and the opportunities were becoming revealed by my diary entries. Going back with a clearer head, a pattern of cash withdrawals was obvious. Before September, Lee took out about £50 a week, but then things started to change. Also, he took out £300 cash from his credit card, which seemed odd. What was that about? It was on a Friday and there was nothing else going on that I'd noted. I brooded on this until I remembered a wood burning stove had been put in the den. We paid cash, and being the the same amount as a Rosa night was sheer coincidence. I had assumed any payments must have used cash withdrawn from his account, but was that correct? Occasionally, Lee repaired furniture for people and sold pieces he had restored, which could have provided a welcome boost for his adventures.

After recording all cash withdrawals, I continued this analytical approach to consider petrol purchases, as the trip to Dundee would be outside the normal mileage. In the file were the fuel receipts showing litres bought and time of purchase. For ease of calculations, I converted to gallons, followed by research on miles to the gallon figures for his car, an elderly Audi saloon. Knowing his mileage to work enabled me to estimate a minimum number of miles per week and from there how many gallons were needed per week. From that baseline, I added in other trips I knew about, including an estimate of the mileage to Dundee. Lurking at the back of my mind was the question of where else he could have gone without my knowledge. According to the bank statements, he had made some purchases at a bookshop in Carlisle. What was he doing there? The detective had proved there were possibilities.

Gradually, I realised this was becoming an obsession, as little post-it notes and odd bits of paper were being covered with repeat calculations of variations on petrol costs, miles to gallon and possible miles driven. Even at work, I found myself scribbling new variations on the theme. My mind had become locked into a loop of questions and possibilities and 'what ifs' until it threatened to overwhelm me. I forced myself to stop. There was sufficient evidence that I didn't have to dot every single 'i'. I asked myself what further proof was needed as if I was desperately trying to find another explanation, trying not to believe it, a form of denial.

I had a break from the spreadsheets by turning to the porn websites listed in the diary. These presented many possibilities, including sex parties in Glasgow, with pictures of tangled bodies writhing around. They were expensive though; widening your sexual experiences was not for the poor. I returned to another mystery in the month before Dundee, with some odd entries on the credit card statement. One was to nochex for £110, which I finally deduced was a method of paying someone at third hand, an intermediary, so to speak. He also withdrew £300 in cash separate to the wood burner amount. According to my diary, he'd gone to a work-related exhibition near Manchester, immediately ruling out Rosa. Who was down there? From his diary, I had jotted down any escorts who were within reasonable distance. He had put a mark by one, Janice. On an escort website, I found a Janice in Manchester, who had her own flat to welcome punters to the best blow job in England, according to her. Really? How does she know? She charged about the same for this experience as Rosa did for a whole night. Perhaps the Nochex was for her with the balance to be paid in cash on arrival. I can see why he changed to Rosa, an awful lot more for his money. Looking at her comments page, it was obvious that men travelling to and from Manchester Airport found her a very satisfying stopping off point before returning to normal family life.

How much of this could I admit to on C day? I needed to be careful, as it would be easy to unwittingly reveal the extent of my discoveries. I decided that the notebook entries, and definitely the painted tin, would be kept a secret. How did I know about the porn though, without admitting to unlocking the cupboard? Could I hint at the hoard, leaving him to doubt whether he had left it unlocked or left magazines lying around? Another oddity took more working out. There were two credit card payments, one for £74.10 and one for £222.29, both to companies based in the US, as exchange rates were given. After a bit of delving and Asking Jeeves, I eventually discovered these were websites selling videos with various themes, all concerning spanking and whipping, with either a man or woman in the dominant role and involving a selection of props. The innocuous-looking video cases I'd seen in the workshop must have disguised these ones. I managed to work out from the exchange rate and the cost of each video that Lee had bought four of them. This information could be deduced from the statements, but I felt wary about challenging him. It was fortunate that by this time it was close to the confrontation deadline. I was having great difficulty adjusting to the way things had escalated, from paper magazines to escorts and S and M videos all in a comparatively short space of time.

All the speculating was put aside as I welcomed the chance to get away for a few days, although visits to my mother were not relaxing. At one time, Lee would come with me, as he had done the previous year for her ninetieth birthday. She was too frail to cope with both of us staying with her, so we booked into a nearby B&B. I had appreciated his company, as she hadn't treated Lee very well in the past. She regarded him as some kind of unpaid servant, although to be fair, she treated me the same. I put up with it, as I was the daughter and she was becoming increasingly unable to do things for herself. Typically, on my arrival, there would be no greeting, just an announcement that a light bulb needed changing or some such. There was one particular occasion that made me vow never to impose Lee on her again. The three of us were standing in her kitchen when she turned to me and asked, 'Would Lee like a cup of tea?' I should have fired straight back and said 'Ask him yourself, he's standing there,' but of course, I didn't. I took the coward's way out and asked him myself. Later we managed to see some humour in the incident and I apologised for her and myself. I told him I wasn't putting him through that again and that future visits would be just me. I imagine he was relieved, but he did worry about me driving down to Surrey on my own, especially in bad weather. My mother went to relatives for Christmas Day now she couldn't travel to us and she was happy with that arrangement. Like me, she was comfortable with her own company and quite content being on her own. I usually went down in early December to avoid possible bad weather later and this was the reason for the current trip.

On the way back, during the monotonous motorway driving,

I considered the C day, two days to go. How do you start off something like that? A gentle lead in, possibly some background to prepare the way, a chronicle of my discoveries? After many miles of churning ideas around, I decided on a concise summary of the core issues. I arrived back, fatigued and beyond caring. I wanted to bring all this to a climax. Wednesday had been designated confrontation day and timed for when Lee got back from work. I couldn't settle to anything, starting simple housekeepery tasks and quickly abandoning them. Beth picked up on my agitation and followed me around, making me more unsettled. Finally, I took her out for a walk, hoping that would calm both of us. As the time approached, I went into the kitchen and filled the kettle, all ready for his arrival. I'd assumed he would come home at the usual time but now worried that I should've found some pretext to check. Too late, I told myself, just get yourself together. Then I heard his car come into the drive and switched on the kettle. As he came through the door, I looked up with a smile as I would normally do. He went through to the hall to hang up his coat and came back to the kitchen where I was pouring water into the teapot. We exchanged a few words about our respective days and then teas poured, I turned away and took a deep breath, hoping he wouldn't notice. I remembered reading somewhere people do this to steady their nerves before going on stage to give a presentation or whatever. I began,

'Will you bring your tea into the living room, please?'

'What?' he asked, puzzled by this change in routine, as we would normally sit at the kitchen table. I went on through to the room saying,

'Just come and sit down in here.'

He shrugged but followed and sat on the sofa while I took a chair. I was feeling completely jangled, probably a bit like a parent finding drugs in a teenager's bedroom, and totally bewildered how to handle the situation.

'I've got something I have to say,' I began. 'Your behaviour over the past few months is completely out of order, beyond anything remotely reasonable.'

He looked at me inquiringly. It was disconcerting that he seemed perfectly relaxed, not giving any hint to how he was feeling. I'm not sure I could have kept up that front. It brought home to me how extremely good he was at deceit, at lying, at living two lives. Surprisingly, I didn't feel any anger, just a powerful sense of betrayal, an end of a delusion, a surrender to the inevitable.

'What on earth do you mean?'

'You know what I mean.'

'No, I don't. What are you getting at?'

Blustering, but not very much.

'I think pornography and prostitution sums it up pretty accurately.'

There was a silence, and a lowering of the head.

'Right.'

Resignedly, followed by more silence.

'How did you find out?'

'It wasn't very difficult.'

'Would you like me to go?'

'Not particularly. Do you want to go?'

'No.'

I didn't want him just walking out the door. Where would he go, for one thing? Help was needed, and the best chance of that was by staying here, although I had no idea what that help entailed. I wasn't thinking of staying in the long term, as everything had gone too far, but wasn't articulating anything very clearly at that moment. I did know I couldn't just let him go out, like a waif and stray. He needed to be at home and, to be quite honest, I didn't want any more disruption just then. Being in the same house would provide a necessary veneer of normality. I wanted to ask why he had done all this stuff, why all the deceit, but I think unconsciously I was afraid it would come down to blaming me. I didn't ask about the porn stuff but did mention that the Dundee visits would have to end while withholding how I knew about them. Evidently, that wasn't a problem, as they were becoming expensive and he was getting a bit bored with Rosa. I refrained from suggesting that boredom could be overcome by choosing another playmate.

It was a pretty miserable evening, not much had actually been said, but what had been was extremely crucial. I think we were both stunned by it and didn't want to elaborate any further, afraid of what might be revealed, just wanted a chance to recover a little. I went off and got us something to eat, pasta and a sauce, which we ate on our laps, watching the news on the television as we would normally do. Thankfully, this was followed by a drama series we had been watching, providing an excuse not to talk. Appetite is the first casualty of mounting tension and stress, but I managed half my pasta despite being aware the effects of a stormy stomach would keep me awake. Lee pushed his food around before giving up and carrying his plate out to the kitchen, coming back a while later with two mugs of tea. Nothing more was said as we both retreated into our inner selves. That suited me, as I didn't want any kind of altercation. I didn't have the energy for it and after the previous few weeks felt emotionally barren. I went off to bed early, as the atmosphere and tension were becoming unbearable, and when he finally came upstairs, I pretended to be asleep.

Over the next day or so, there was no proper discussion, just a tweaking out of snippets of information. He was curious about how I found out and obviously frustrated by my vague replies to his questions. I suppose we were both at fault in our reticence to make a challenge. I had asked that any pornography could be removed, as our shared property should be a porn-free zone. I felt strongly about this and probably came over more forceful than I intended. Fortunately there was no objection, mere acceptance, and the next weekend, Lee disappeared into the workshop, followed by an expanding heap of black bin bags appearing at the entrance. This provided visible proof 'That' cupboard was being cleared. After the initial discovery, I hadn't looked any further, but the growing pile lead me to suspect there had been other hidden caches. Clearly, they wouldn't fit into one wheelie bin but would need spreading over several weekly collections.

As I have said before, he withdraw into himself if anything got difficult and I let him do that, realising I had the same tendencies myself. I was complicit because any challenge from me would have been met with lies and I didn't need any more of those. It was a miserable, eggshell shrewn time.

Confrontation | Therapy

Rachael. We have arrived at the main dramatic event, but before turning to that, let's look briefly at the creation of the spreadsheet. It could be viewed as a straightforward analytical exercise, but it soon becomes obvious it's nothing of the kind. You deal with numbers as part of your work, analysing figures is second nature to you, and normally, there would be little emotional involvement. This is different, creating a sense of conflict between impersonal analysis and the deeply emotional and personal challenge of what is being revealed.

Sheena. Yes, I was aware of that difference at the time.

R. Very unsettling, as you are witnessing someone playing out a separate, parallel life, a secret clandestine life, away from you. You no longer have the basics to hang on to. In nautical terms, your anchor is dragging. That was very hard, as deceit was a significant factor for you. It's often the case, that revelations about an affair or financial misdeeds, for instance, are not the main issue. It's the scale of the deceit, the deliberate, carefully planned deceit, that hurts the most.

S. I think that's right. And of course, my imagination ran riot. Normally I would be clearheaded, thinking logically, but here I saw the figures without any cognizance, my brain refused all messages, too scrambled to process. My thoughts would go spiralling off. Felt a bit like when you blow up a balloon and then let go, and it goes crazy, whoosing around uncontrollably, and you are frantically trying to grab it. It was a bit like that. Spinning off. And I had to work hard at calming down again.

R. These are all classic signs of stress, as I am sure you realise. After all, you were trying to deal with a series of traumatic events.

S. And for example, I got myself completely tied up in knots about the fuel, the fuel thing, that really got to me. I got so obsessed with the calculations as if I was trying to find something to hang on to and say yes, this is something concrete.

R. Exactly. You didn't have that. But to your credit, you got through it, you managed.

S. Yes, I suppose so, although it didn't feel much like managing. I wasn't going to let it all get the better of me though.

R. No, you're a strong person. Let's turn now to the major event, the confrontation. During the time beforehand, you worried about what approach you would take. You wisely decided not to reveal the full extent of your explorations, which could well have triggered an angry response. You had set a date, which you adhered to. It's very easy to procrastinate and get onto that wretched treadmill and become stuck in a cycle of excuse making, captive but made miserable by not escaping. On the day, you used just two key words to sum up his activities, pornography and prostitution. He had no answer except going on the defensive by asking how you found out. The whole of that exchange was showing the classic sequence of denial, bluster, capitulation and resignation. I'm left wondering what was not said, the lack of reaction on Lee's part. He seemed more interested in how you found out than facing the problem.

S. Yes, I could almost see his mind trying to figure out how I knew. Perhaps he thought someone at work had found out and told me.

R. I imagine he was seriously worried about how much you knew. He offered practical answers to your questions while keen to justify his actions and divert some blame on you. However, he took on board what you said and cleared out the workshop, which suggests he was trying to redeem himself to some extent. Basically though, he doesn't want to engage, has withdrawn into himself, showing a familiar pattern of behaviour. When you were considering what approach to take, did you consider possible outcomes? What had you expected?

S. I hadn't thought that through; just concentrated on the first part. I was a bit afraid in case there was an angry explosion, although confident there wouldn't be actual violence. That had never been an issue. I don't think I had any clear idea of the consequences, as it was a completely new experience. I suppose in some ways it was an anticlimax, leaving both of us in an uneasy temporary truce. We couldn't simply pretend the confrontation hadn't happened, but for the time being, we reverted to our standard behaviours of withdrawing to safety.

R. As you say, an uneasy truce. We are left with the aftermath of the confrontation, and this could be a good time to consider background influences to find explanations for Lee's reponse and his behaviour. In addition to the pornography, a further element has appeared with the videos from the States and their spanking theme. I think it is pertinent here to repeat that pornography dependency is not triggered by a desire for sex, it is not principally about sex, so perhaps we should look at what it is about and how that ties up with Lee's background. Is that OK, or do you think we are going off the subject too much?

S. No, I would like to explore what his motivations were and how he got to the point he had.

R. Well, we know he used porn before, but there is an escalation into escorts and S and M. Perhaps it is worth putting things in perspective, as nothing you have described is extreme or even illegal and, more importantly, does not involve children. But I am emphatically not condoning this or playing down its significance.

S. Good grief, no! If there had been any hint of children, I would have gone to the police, no doubt whatsoever.

R. Yes, and you would have been right. But what you did find was shocking enough to you. I'm not trying to minimise that shock, all these things are relative. Let's look at the use of porn in general and then how Lee fits the pattern. As we discussed in an earlier session, use of pornography is about self-soothing when people lack confidence and feel they are neither valued or loved. Those negative feelings start very early, becoming ingrained in our view of ourselves. Conversely, some people do have very settled and secure upbringings, are certain of their self-worth and enjoy a loving and supportive childhood. I would say surprisingly few actually, but that's just my view. Turning to Lee, I think you mentioned at one point he was brought up by his mother because his father had left early on.

S. Yes, that's right, when he was about ten or eleven, I think. He just buggered off, as Lee put it. Although he didn't like talking about him, it was clear Lee had no time for his dad and there had been no contact since he'd left.

R. The early teens, puberty, is a critical period for development, especially for boys. These are uncertain and bewildering times, as so much is happening physically, with hormones causing major upsets. If there is anything else going on in a young person's life, it can have a significant effect on their confidence and sense of security.

S. He had a younger sister, and his mother was left with both of them without any financial support from her husband. She worked full time and her parents helped look after the children, but they worked too. They were a relatively poor family.

R. As Lee's mother was working, she probably didn't have the time or energy to provide the support he needed.

S. No, I suppose not. He was reluctant to talk about his child-hood, but occasionally, if we were relaxing by the fire, warmed by food and wine, he would be more forthcoming. It was obvious he respected his mother and appreciated her efforts to look after them all, at least in retrospect. He would bring his sister home from school to an empty house, which must have been a lonely time.

R. Yes, he was bearing a lot of responsibility and I imagine took it all very seriously. He didn't receive the attention he needed, instead having to grow up pretty quickly, losing some of his childhood along the way. Did he say what had happened at school?

S. I think that was a bit mixed. He was more intelligent than his family and got a scholarship to a very good boys grammar school. He felt out of it, didn't fit in, as many of the boys came from middle-class families, although he never mentioned any bullying. In fact, he made some good friends and a couple of them came to our wedding. It was the teachers who gave him a hard time. Evidently, he didn't do much work, messed about, probably came over as surly and stubborn. That would have annoyed the staff, so he got punished, physically, quite frequently. He got some O Levels and finally realised that unless he started doing some work, passed some A Levels and went to university, he could end up in a local factory. He begun working seriously and got some mischievous pleasure from getting good grades against all expectations. He got a kick out of that.

R. An 'up yours' mentality, and good for him. This is telling us that he was a bit of a loner but determined, a stubborn character. He couldn't go to his mother for support and comfort, so was forced to rely on his own resources in order to keep himself safe. No doubt his grandparents gave love and nurturing but were limited in their time with him. He needed to be self-reliant. Does this sound familiar, as I think this is what you did as well?

S. Yes, you're right. Odd that with such different backgrounds, we had the basics in common.

R. That is true. You may not have articulated these similarities before, but unconsciously you had a shared need, a need to be valued for your own sakes. Both of you sought a solution within yourselves, you with your imagination, him with pornography, both acting to anaesthetise against various challenges such as loneliness, anxiety, fear and loss. In Lee's case, using porn became a habit, a familiar solace whenever life became difficult. We could say it was acting as his security blanket. Do you remember the character in the Peanuts cartoons, what was he called?

S. Linus? Yes, Linus and his blanket held up to his head, his security blanket. I had the equivalent as a child, a piece of gauze cloth. I liked those cartoons, particularly Snoopy sitting on top of his kennel pronouncing to the world.

R. Yes, I can just picture him. Well, most people need the equivalent of a security blanket in one form or another. So, things went trundling on like that for many years and then something changed, things escalated, increasing his dependency. Changing from paper to other media, such as video and internet, immediately opens up greater opportunities and infinite variety, to the point of being overwhelming but very exciting.

S. Yes, that makes sense, but I am still baffled by any particular event setting it off. I think it was more likely a gradual buildup of loss of confidence, a feeling of being on his own, falling back on his own resources.

R. I agree, although there had been major changes, for instance moving from England to Scotland, a major culture change for him, although not for you, from one kind of life to another. You are no longer based at home but each going to work in very different environments. Maybe back in Hereford, the home base was also a security base, but you no longer had that. There is an emphasis on things away from home, things you are doing separately.

S. Yes, you're right, that's how it was evolving. When you are in the middle of it though, you don't appreciate what's happening.

R. You say 'you', but aren't we talking about 'I'? 'I was in the middle of it'. People often do this as a way of stepping back, as a defence against acknowledging what is happening. Lee's way of dealing with these changes was to self-care by turning to his time-honoured solace. It's his way to protect himself and defend against fears of abandonment and loss of a former, more secure life. In fact, both of you were right there in the midst of these changes, colluding as joint conspirators, all unconsciously, of course.

S. That's hard to take, but I recognise the truth of it. I was increasingly getting involved in events away from home and this could be viewed, I suppose, as saying he wasn't enough for me. I needed other mental stimulation. At the time I just did these things without considering deeper motives or, to be honest, the effect on him. And because he wasn't good at talking, we didn't have any discussions.

R. Let's not do any blaming. All we are trying to do is understand what was happening. Both of you were reacting to the changes according to your own defence systems. Nearly all our behaviours from birth are defensive in some way, either as defending off a perceived threat from outside or by defending against a potential internal threat. Take hunger for instance, young babies use very effective manoeuvres when they want to be fed. They have few ways of communicating but use what they do have to very good effect, including full-blooded yelling. That usually does the trick. In childhood and beyond, we each develop manoeuvres of our own to defend and protect ourselves. A security blanket, in whatever form, is part of that defence system. I could say more on this theme, but we have strayed into the theoretical and I think that is enough for now.

S. It's given me a lot to think about and no doubt some of it will be difficult. It needs to be done though. But, you're right, I think that's enough for now.

R. Yes, I agree. We said at the start of today that we would look at Lee's background. We have done that, so let's leave it there for now. One of the drawbacks to this method is that I have no idea of the content of the next narratives, but obviously you do. Can I take it there will be other opportunities for further discussion on today's topics?

S. Yes, very much so, I'm afraid.

R. Good, we'll leave it there then.

Session Seven

Limbo | Narrative

POST-CONFRONTATION, TIME WAS suspended, a liminal
time. Behind me lay a trail of shocks, but ahead was a space
without belief, an agnostic time. Those 'D' words, Down, Desolate, Despondent, threatened to rule.

I questioned Lee about needing Dundee but he made the
point that as I no longer wanted him sexually he could not just
stop. Rather than an affair, which would have been more of a
relationship, he used escorts. He made it sound very reasonable
and thereby exonerated himself. He didn't want to give up sex,
'I can't just stop' or leave so had no other option. The inference
was clear, this was down to me. I kept quiet about the notebook
while hinting at knowing the internet and email activity. I had
no means of checking if his computer use had stopped and a
question mark remained about any local encounters.

Shortly before Christmas, I met Jane to tell her about the confrontation. She had good news, as Robert had joined a holiday
park, helping to market their activities programme for the next
season. This tied in well with their previous business in Cumbria
running cycling holidays. I mentioned I had suggested couple
counselling to Lee but that his response was 'I'm not having some
bloody shrink walking around inside my head.' Jane queried if I

had any hope of rebuilding the marriage. Up to that point, I had avoided such a blunt choice but now acknowledged that breaking up was a reality.

Thus began a limbo time, skittering around each other, nothing being said that could spark an emotional outburst, just holding it together on a superficial level – 'Shall I get a pizza from Safeway on the way home?' for example. We usually spent the Christmas holiday by ourselves, as neither of us were close to any familly members. We always made a fuss over the Christmas Day meal and old habits die hard. We had champagne before the meal, opening presents in front of a roaring fire before going through to the dining room for a feast. That year the main event was a joint of gammon, glazed and studded with cloves and baked to a rich, deep golden perfection in the Rayburn. We pulled crackers and donned hats before struggling with the pudding and finishing off with chocolates and nuts. For a suspended thread of time, it was possible, almost, to believe we were a normal contented couple.

After the holiday period, I often cried on the way back from work. I would rack up the anguish by playing Kris Kristofferson's mournful songs like 'For the Good Times' and 'Nobody Wins' or James Grant with his 'Does It All Add Up To Nothing?' Paradoxically, piling on the misery seemed to have an uplifting effect. It was hard keeping my personal misery hidden from the cheerful front expected at work. Most of the time I managed it, although one longstanding client asked if anything was wrong. I simply said Lee and I were having some problems and he nodded sympathetically as if he had guessed. He asked no more, simply laid a light hand on my shoulder as he went by to get us some coffee. Unspoken support, but it meant so much.

Home life was not good, with several weeks of merely

surviving. I used to look forward to arriving back, but now there were occasions when the car slowed involuntarily on nearing home. Beth, on my lap, looked up inquiringly when I turned off before our lane and parked by the estuary. I sat for a bit, no inclination to do anything, but eventually dog responsibilities took over. We walked along the shore, calmed by the rhythm of the waves swooping in, before the gentle, wet rattle of the pebbles left by the retreating water. It was reflection time, helping to put the sadness aside and provide momentum once home. By now, the evenings were lighter, so time could be spent outdoors in the garden or Lee would be in the workshop with both doors open. Otherwise we watched repeats of programmes we had enjoyed in the past like *Lovejoy* and *Last of the Summer Wine*.

We found excuses to eat out and I can claim I have cried in all the Italian-themed restaurants in Dumfries. At one meal, I asked him how he'd managed to leave work early for the trips to Dundee, about a hundred and forty-five miles. Evidently, he just 'went missing', as he could be in one of several places on the site apart from his workshop. I remembered Andy had mentioned this a while ago without realising the significance. He had been in the office asking for Lee, but been told he was missing as if a common occurrence. I suggested that he had enjoyed the excitement of planning the assignations, the journey and the thrills of the encounters. I appreciated all that, and he readily agreed with a wistful smile. Bizarrely we resumed having sex, which was urgent, itch scratching rather than lovemaking, but soon reverted to occasional quickies. I wanted to put time aside to lie together, taking things slowly, but that never happened. About this time, belatedly and unbelievably, it occurred to me I should get myself tested. It illustrates how jangled my mind was that I hadn't considered it before. I presented myself down at my doctor's, but she assured me that the prostitutes in Dumfries and Galloway were pretty clean and not to worry about Aids. Her expression changed when I explained that Lee had used women from other parts of the country, and she proceeded to take samples and swabs. To my relief, they came back negative.

One day, a few weeks later, I was feeling particularly despondent. I was due in Castle Douglas that morning to prepare some reports. I was honour bound to go but couldn't summon up the energy required to put on my positive Mrs Fixit persona when I just wanted to crawl into a corner. I got myself together enough to phone and say, 'Sorry, something's come up. I'll be a bit late, but I'll definitely be there.'

'That's no problem, nae bother. Will be glad to see you when you can.'

By this time, I was far enough down the pit shaft to see the bottom but with a few rungs left. I needed a supportive, calming voice get me through the next few hours. I was trapped, struggling under a blanket, not a light, modern version but more akin to Army issue, heavy, dark, slightly damp and bristly.

Fortunately, I remembered a charity for people in a crisis so I phoned the local branch and a recorded message told me I would be transferred elsewhere. A woman answered and gently asked how I was feeling, obviously checking if I was suicidal. I assured her no, but I needed help, as I was very upset and confused. She said she could hear that. I explained that after being married for twenty-six years, I had recently discovered my husband was using pornography and seeing other women. Then it tumbled out about Lee's behaviour and the escorts, although not at great length. She began by sounding sympathetic but then questioned why he needed to do this. I admitted I'd lost interest in sex, although, at this point, I felt we were getting off the subject. It was my current state of mind that was the issue, not the whys and wherefores; I simply wanted a calming influence to talk me into a better place. This conversation wasn't helping me feel better, but then it took a bizarre downhill turn.

'But if you weren't interested in sex, what did you expect him to do?'

'Not go with escorts!'

'Well, maybe not, but it's being a bit unfair not to make an effort and keep our male partners happy. I'm in a new relationship and it's really exciting doing new things and learning how to please each other. It's arousing, energising; perhaps you need to be more proactive.'

At that point, I held the phone away from me, staring at it open-mouthed. What was this woman doing? I had rung up to get some support and yet here she was being judgemental of me, putting me in the wrong. She might have a point, but it wasn't an appropriate stance in my present fragile state. This woman could have sent me down the road towards ending it all. I found this quite shocking, hard to believe. She continued talking about her wonderful new partner, apparently oblivious to the effect she had.

'If you've lost your interest in sex, there is a female Viagra out there now, a plant from the Amazon. I've tried it to get an extra boost and it does work. On the internet, there are other techniques such as for oral sex that could be helpful.' She hadn't sounded as though she needed any boosting, but I wrote down the name of the magic potion. I thought this charity was supposed to help at times of crisis, not to blame the caller for their woes and tell them to get sex lessons. By that point I'd had enough, it was unreal. I thanked her and put the phone down.

It was one of those situations when you're not sure whether to laugh or cry, although it did have the effect of making me stronger. I laughed rather than cried; it was so unbelievable, but it gave me the strength to go off to work. But was that what I needed? A rather risky form of therapy, I would've thought. It could just as easily have gone the other way, as I was made out to be inadequate and, of course, my man was entitled to find excitement elsewhere. Righteous indignation took over, swept me out of the house, grapping coat and car keys en route and into the car and away. I slowed down after a mile or so, realising I could have driven straight into a tree, desolate that I'd spent nearly fifty years in sexual incompetence.

Later, questions crept to the surface in the insidious way that doubt and misery often do. Being naturally of a curious disposition, I got onto Ask Jeeves and discovered that a female Viagra did indeed exist, although I baulked at the idea of ordering any. Techniques for satisfying your man orally were freely available, but I stuck to words rather than diagrams or videos. One site pointed out that giving a mind blowing oral experience was the greatest gift a woman could give a man. That had a very demoralising effect because here I was, sixty-two and a complete amateur. I'd had a few oral encounters with no complaints from the recipients, but Lee had never indicated any interest in that aspect. I'd been grateful, as I didn't find it a pleasurable experience. I questioned whether an aversion to having semen in my mouth was a major failing, and should I try to overcome it? But it was too late now.

We continued our coexistence but without any discussion. I was aware we avoided spending time alone together. Anything rather than being in a house heavily charged with tears and unanswered questions. We both enjoyed Eddi Reader's music, so on one Saturday evening, we took ourselves up to the Glasgow Concert Halls with a room, twin, booked at the Express Holiday Inn. This was a welcome escape, a time away, out of time. To emphasise the separation from our usual lives, I use the present tense to describe this event.

Eddi has sung her Robert Burns songs and we find ourselves wandering downhill along Renfield Street. We turn into a pub that is packed inside, but we find a couple of stools and squeeze in between two groups of young people. Lee chooses a pint of Orkney's Red MacGregor from the impressive collection of hand pumps, but I settle for a dry white wine. We spend some time discussing the concert before the alcohol has its usual effect of dismantling the defences. The mischief questions come creeping up into the light, persistent in their particular brand of flagellation. Why am I going to spoil a perfectly good evening? Can't I let the Rosa business die a natural death? I cannot help myself; the need to know is too persistent. I need to know what she was like, what did they talk about, because although knowledge can be power, in this case, it is comfort. Knowledge as comfort, to give structure, something definite to replace the nebulous weaving of shadows. Tonight I sense he is going to humour me and give me straightforward answers. I notice some minimally dressed girls in a group near us.

'Did Rosa dress like that?' I ask.

'No, of course not. She looked ordinary. She'd arrive wearing an anorak-type coat.'

He moves on quickly to a new topic.

'She wanted to take photos, but I wasn't having that.'

'Photos? What on earth for?'

'Her husband wanted them so he could send them to the States, trying to sell them. Trouble is, so many people are doing that now, there's not much of a demand and they don't pay very well. Evidently, there is quite a market for amateur photos as opposed to the professional ones.'

I look interested, feeling drawn into showing some sympathy for their failing business idea, but perhaps not. Although the idea of natural, un-photoshopped pornography is quite a thought.

'Oh, right, so she was asking you for marketing advice?'

I am trying hard to keep the sarcasm out of my voice. He replies in a neutral tone, so perhaps I have succeeded.

'No, of course not. Her husband manages her website and selling photos.'

'Does her husband work in IT?'

'No, not sure what he does. She has a part-time job, works in a local café.'

Evidently, she has two children.

'She used to talk about her kids; there were various problems with them at school.'

I struggle to picture this cosy chat, lying side by side in bed sipping a glass of wine. He goes on.

'I think she welcomed someone to talk to. It was a bit like counselling really.'

Now I know he's humouring me but don't argue the point. It's bizarre, discussing his favourite escort's domestic problems as if we're talking about a conventional family enterprise. I am almost fooled into thinking it is normal but am brought up short. I am wondering what she tells the children when she disappears on Friday nights for her all-nighters, Mum's on night shift? I think of her website photos, where her face is blacked out, no wonder, as I can imagine the sheer horror of a child finding its mother's body displayed on the internet. This is not in any way a normal family business. I've had my information fix, so keep quiet after that, but I'm appalled by the juxtaposition of the surreal humour of the situation with the reality that my husband visits escorts with relish.

Back at home, the skirmishing continued. It gradually filtered through that he was very resentful towards my questions, thinking I was trying to humiliate him. I assured him I wasn't, but he remained suspicious.

Although I had written off any chance of rebuilding our lives, I suggested to Lee we could try couple counselling, as I thought it would help him to face his issues. He reluctantly agreed and I started investigating local possibilities. I arranged an appointment for us and we duly presented ourselves at the organisation's office. Our counsellor was a middle-aged woman, conservatively dressed, called Rita. We went through an information gathering session, which culminated with the inevitable question of why we were there. Lee had contributed little up to now, so I suggested I gave a summary of what had happened. He sat stony-faced while I told Rita the basics of drifting apart and his infidelity without going into details, as at that point she was more interested in getting an idea of our background and everyday lives. At the second session, we were encouraged to give more detail, but as Lee was reluctant to talk, it fell to me to give the story – porn, escorts, the trust issues and the deceits. I could sense he was getting a bit annoyed, irritated, as I realised I was painting him in a bad light. He burst out,

'I've said I'm sorry, I've told you. You keep asking me, but I've told you all this. It was just Dundee, Newcastle and Manchester.'

And then he abruptly stopped, as if he was willing me not to pick up on what he had just said, but I had and was finding it difficult to believe.

'Newcastle?' I retorted in tones strongly reminiscent of Lady Bracknell and the handbag.

'But I told you about that,' he protested, desperately trying to put the genie back in the bottle.

'No, you didn't, you did not mention Newcastle. When was it?'

'Oh, it was just once, can't remember exactly when.'

Rita couldn't quite keep her neutral expression. She would have been used to tales of infidelities and affairs but perhaps not this multi-tentacled beast that Lee was coming out with. As soon as you think you have it pinned down and can see the whole of it, another tentacle edges furtively out. I think that was at the heart of it, I couldn't get hold of anything of substance and, of course, he did not want to give me any more. Rita realised there was no point in trying to get further detail, so instead talked about trust and how difficult it was, once trust had been damaged, to build it up again. I thought destroyed would be more accurate. It was left for us to decide how we wanted to continue and she suggested individual sessions as a possibility. I think we all knew we would not be going back.

I wish, in one of those sessions, Lee could have said he was really sorry and then asked Rita if she could help us work through things. He never did that or gave any sense of engaging with the process. He was sorry for hurting me, but there was no hint of any shame for his behaviour. He apologised to me and at one point said he had the most wonderful woman in the world and all he had done was shat upon her from a great height. A dramatic thing to say, but meaningless, as no actions followed. Words alone were hollow. It sounded ironic now, but previously he had said I was all that really mattered to him, he would be nothing without me. I'm not sure what I wanted but probably looked for him to meet me halfway and work together towards a solution. As it was, he refused to go back for more counselling, he retreated into himself without offering any suggestions about resolving the problems. Perhaps he hoped it would settle down over time, so he didn't have to be proactive.

Limbo | Therapy

Rachael. This narrative is fragmented, flowing less than the previous ones, but as you said, it was a liminal time full of uncertainty.

Sheena. Yes, that whole period was seriously odd.

R. So let's work through the piece. It's a pity Lee refused further couple counselling, but it only works if both parties engage with the process. I suspect Lee couldn't do that, as he was feeling seriously adrift by that point.

S. Yes, I think so and I didn't appreciate that.

R. And you are facing the reality of breaking up, although I'm not sure you have come to terms with it emotionally. Head decided but not your heart. The painful ritual of Christmas must have been excruciating at times, but necessary.

S. It was painful, but I was grateful we could spend the day together, and in the afternoon, we escaped with Beth for a walk.

R. OK, Lee is obviously sorry he's hurt you but not sorry for all the stuff he did. He is not admitting shame. Shame is imposed internally while guilt is external. From the start, we seek the approval of those closest to us, but if we experience humiliation and criticism, we feel shame. We haven't measured up, we've let people down, we are useless. As we talked before, this is the same type of background that can lead to porn dependency. Lee wants to be valued and loved but is too stubborn to admit it. Denial then leads to other facets of shame, withdrawal or self-righteousness. At the confrontation, there was no apology. Instead, the first reaction was indignation. He attempted to hide his true needs by denial, before retreating into silence.

S. And he justified his actions over the escorts.

R. Yes, that's right. Let's have a look at the couple implications of all this. You both had similar early experiences, leading to each of you sharing an idea, albeit unconsciously. A dream that you could work through the past, remove the uncertainties and allow both of you to gain confidence and self-esteem. This was a shared unconscious idea, a shared phantasy in the sense you both imagined this could happen. For a long time, I think it did work. In Hereford, you had a mutual support system but were particularly vulnerable to threats from outside upsetting the equilibrium. A certain amount of similar background brought you together and kept you together. Non-communication was the fall back position, which was tolerated and accepted in each other. The move to Scotland presented new challenges, new country, new culture and new work. You welcomed those changes, but Lee felt threatened by them. Change as a threat or a challenge: two opposing views of life, you could say.

S. I do like challenge and I do like change. I wonder if that blinded me to his reactions to the move. I seriously underestimated the extent he relied on me for mental strength. In reality, I had a lot of self-doubt and was surprised and pleased if I received praise for anything. My greater energy and enthusiasm may have disguised the internal doubts while Lee simply retreated and appeared sullen and rude. I didn't fully recognise his vulnerability.

R. Yes. He was used to falling back on his own resources, as you were too, but in a different way. As Lee felt more threatened, he was taken back in his mind to how things had been, how he had felt then, feelings of being humiliated by events. There was lack of support from his mother, as she didn't have the time for him.

S. She worked full time, so few opportunities for playing with the children or having fun. He was expected to do some of the chores, so not allowed to be a child.

R. And I imagine he took those responsibilities seriously. He wanted to please, gain approval. Turning to the more general; early in life, we all form a set of beliefs about ourselves and our place in the world, a distillation of experiences both positive and negative. The more negative the beliefs the more adverse effect they will have on our development. I suggest both of you have common beliefs, such as, 'I'm not important for myself', 'I am alone', 'Don't be me', 'I have to help others to get attention'. It doesn't follow that these beliefs are true, and as adults, we can challenge them and replace the unhelpful ones with something more positive. Unfortunately not everyone can do this and instead remain trapped by their past assumptions.

S. Does that mean by welcoming change I was open to updating my beliefs while Lee was finding it more difficult? Is that one of the reasons we were growing apart?

R. I think that played a part, yes. It is up to each one of us to choose, to change or not, as ultimately we are responsible for ourselves. Also, if our beliefs are negative and detrimental to us, paradoxically, the fear of losing the known can overcome the potential benefits from facing the unknown.

S. And the negative messages would have come back as the distance between us grew. You mentioned the need to please, do things to get approval. This sounds a bit trivial, but I've remembered an incident soon after we met at university. Lee was interested in making things, even back then. I happened to mention I could do with a bookcase in my room and there was one at my parents' house. It was a bit dilapidated and Lee offered to sand it down and varnish it; he was in a self-catering block, so had more space. I really appreciated it. Is that what you are saying, a need to give?

R. Yes, good example. Let's look at the Glasgow trip. I agree it was right to use the present tense, giving a stark sense of stepping out of time. The picture of an escort's domestic arrangements intrigued me, but I was seriously concerned about her children. As you discovered, it is horrifyingly easy to find details on the internet. Were those children at risk? I would have thought so. I think Lee was enjoying this, teasing you, being mostly truthful, and you got your information fix. In some ways, it was funny.

S. I was too immersed in incredulity at the time to register the humour, but I did in retrospect.

R. You kept returning to the Dundee visits and Rosa, the need to know. This is a common response in these circumstances, a form of self-torture.

S. I was aware of that but couldn't stop digging.

R. There are hints in the narrative that you tuned in to the excitement aspect of the Dundee trips, but not that Lee was seeking sexual variety. I imagine a man spending the night with a prostitute would usually expect more than the missionary position. After you resumed sex, you preferred a tantric approach rather than something more rumbustious, revealing an expectation gap between the two of you. You appreciate Lee seeking excitement but shrink back from it yourself. Is that a clue to your loss of interest?

S. I'm not sure, I've been trying to make sense of it. There was a gradual deterioration from about a year before the time of the first narrative. When we made love and it was good, he would say 'We need to do this more often' and I'd agree but not with my heart in it. To be fair, he did try to talk about it, he would say, 'We need to do something about this.' I took the lazy option and did nothing.

R. It appears something else was going on, otherwise why not work together to put things right? You had been very close and loving previously. Sexual behaviour and attitudes can act as a metaphor for other aspects of personal life and I think this could be happening here.

And next, we have another bizarre situation, the telephone call to the helpline. That woman was unprofessional, but thank goodness, you saw the humorous side.

S. I was surprised by her, but at least it was educational!

R. In some ways. But it started you thinking, questioning yourself. You were not doing that previously, but here you are considering oral sex techniques.

S. I was amazed too, as I was forced to re-examine my attitudes, but... I didn't consider suggesting changes to Lee.

R. No, and what would have happened if you had? I suppose one possibility for variety is dressing up games that can exclude sexual practices. People often introduce a theatrical element into their sex lives, dressing up and playing roles, for instance. Many couples find it very enjoyable and exciting. You mentioned before that Rosa's outfit reminded you of Tom Sharpe and his exuberant characters.

S. They were very funny, but I can't see myself performing like that. Too inhibited, I think.

R. A lot of ideas swirling around and some of them unsettling. We are getting near the crux, so exploring further now may escalate in unhelpful ways. Let's pause there and continue next time.

S. Yes, I think I've gone down that route as far as I want to today. Need some time to work out how to deal with all this.

Session Eight

Creativity | Narrative

BY NOW, IT WAS SUMMER. If I was at home during the day, I sat on the steps leading to the lower part of the garden. A relaxing time observing the busy lives around me. Birds flitting, bees and butterflies hovering and the myriad of tiny creatures flying and crawling.

Some years previously, Andy had found a set of stone slabs of random shades and colours to form a terrace. Lee had added a pagoda-like structure with a glass roof and open sides, while I had added a softening element with evergreen Japanese honey-suckle and wisteria. In the evenings, during that time, we took our supper out there, a bowl of rice and curry or a slice of pizza with salad. No talking was required, as watching the evening sun sharpening the planes and angles of trees and estuary mud was ample distraction. A parody of a companionable silence. At week-ends, we wandered out to an NTS reserve, with woodland walks giving views out to sea. There was no hiding the two-dimensional aspect of this period. Below the deceptively innocuous surface, we couldn't ignore the urgency for change. There was no status quo to maintain, only fragility, and far too much had happened to make recovery possible. Only major decisions would suffice, this was the time to face finality.

The logical step, the decision to sell the house, edged up from the unconscious, by an osmotic process. The rationale was to downsize and repay the mortgage, albeit a small one. When we presented this idea to each other, it was obvious we had been thinking along the same lines but were reluctant to say much, for fear of upsetting the fragile balance. Our house was not particularly large, but we had enhanced it without detracting from the original features. The value had gone up considerably with the market being buoyant at the time. The garden was a third of an acre, partly rocky outcrops covered in heather and gorse but mostly good productive soil. The property had that most important feature, location, being in a quiet cul-de-sac on a hillside, overlooking water and hills. We could afford a similar size house, a much smaller garden and in a less favoured position.

I would miss the garden, as it was largely my creation. In my view, it was an investment, not in a financial sense, but a contribution to nurturing the natural world. Over the previous few months, I had lost my enthusiasm and commitment without registering it. I needed to get that back temporarily to make some effort in tidying up outside before putting the house on the market. The weeding and deadheading had a welcome therapeutic effect while keeping a balance to prevent shy modest plants from being overwhelmed by more robust neighbours. Lee started to sort out his workshop, using contacts with wood people to sell some of the surplus tools and materials. I could not imagine him giving up all the private and personal woodworking jobs. Lee got property details from the estate agents and we started looking at houses. This immediately prompted me to think I needed to make sure we didn't buy one. He appeared to assume we should still be together, but how could we be when nothing had been resolved? Was he really expecting us to coexist under the same roof, in our current separated worlds? I didn't want to bring things to a head when ambiguity would not be an option, and true to form, we didn't discuss it. Perhaps he saw moving as a welcome diversion from everything else, but I saw it as a solution to our predicament.

There was little communication between us and one particular incident struck me as odd but not atypical. We were in the kitchen one afternoon and I had made the inevitable pot of tea. I placed a mug in front of him on the table and sat down, cradling my own mug, as the tea was too hot for drinking. Lee made no movement or response. I broke the discomfort of the silence by some mundane comment, inviting an acknowledgement if not necessarily an answer. I started to wonder if he had heard me but quickly dismissed that as ridiculous. I sneaked a look at him, but no response. The stillness ticked on and he did nothing to disturb it. Beth in her bed by the Rayburn stirred in her sleep, as her world continued without any concern with ours. That lack of response was like a blow. How could I have so little impact – in fact, no impact at all – on the man next to me? It was if a glass screen had dropped down between us. I picked up my mug, got up and walked out of the room, closing the door behind me. It was then the tears started. The most shocking thing is that Lee gave no sign whatsoever of registering my presence. I think this is incredibly hard to do; there is usually an involuntary flicker of the eyes, a slight movement of the head, a muscle twitch to acknowledge another person is there, even if you don't wish to speak to them. There was nothing.

During this time, I had no idea what Lee might be doing now he had cleared out the workshop and had no opportunities for nights away. I was left considering any local activities and possibilities at work. Eventually, I gave in to the temptation and looked in the workshop. As expected, there was nothing obvious; the cupboard doors standing open with nothing inside, flaunting the emptiness. On the bench were some manuals and woodworking magazines. One looked a bit more worn than the others, well thumbed, and opening it out revealed sheets of paper covered with Lee's handwriting. On closer inspection, I realised they were handwritten stories. At first, I assumed these were stories copied out of books, but it become obvious he'd written them himself. In several, he was driving along in his car followed by various scenarios of what happened when he reached his destination. In one example, the page was headed with a list of dramatis personae before continuing with the story. The principle character, John, was an employee summoned to the boss's office. His first reaction was, have I done something wrong? He needn't have worried. The boss, Mr Jackson, is all smiles and wanting to help, as he knows John's girlfriend had left him. Mr Jackson's wife is in the office, needing chastisement, and she would love John to beat her. The woman cries out with the whipping but is very grateful, and as a reward, the boss lets John have sex with her. There were a couple of other stories in a similar vein.

My first reaction was one of bewilderment, closely followed by a reluctant respect for creativity. Like the video scenarios, they were all very formulaic, yet I was sad he felt the need to do this. I had wandered into his intensely private fantasy world, leaving me with sorrow and compassion. I asked myself where those themes had come from. Where were the clues? They were there ready to emerge. There'd been a few times Lee had taken a thin leather belt of mine and stroked my leg with it, very gently working his way up to my upper thigh and beyond. That had been very titillating in a low-key teasing way, but then he had struck me with it, not hard, but enough for me to object. It made me wary of anything worse happening.

Up came another memory, tucked away, as it had frightened me at the time. Back in Herefordshire, one of our outbuildings had a hayloft supported by wooden posts. One particular day, Lee was helping me lift sacks of poultry feed into the metal storage bins. Suddenly, he came up behind me, grabbed my arms and tried to tie me to a post with a rope. All the primitive instincts of fighting a danger came right to the fore and I thrust him off, sending him reeling backwards with the startled look of a head-light hare. I reacted particularly strongly, partly from surprise and partly from an inherent fear of being tied up and powerless. He quickly realised I was seriously scared and was very apologetic, insisting it was only a bit of fun. I just looked at him, unable to find suitable words for a reply, as fun it was not. He never suggested or attempted anything like it again. Those memories served to recall links all the way through, and I had been naïve to ignore them, as if they were nothing to do with me. They obviously were and had now made their presence felt in a vivid and upsetting way. And then there was the biting... I'll leave that for later.

Lee had always been moody, and during this time, he was unpredictable and withdrawn, hardly surprising given everything that was going on. I had noticed he went through cycles of be-haviour and an incident occurred during one of his withdrawal states. It was a dreich day, dark with heavy rain, not particularly cold, but we had lit the wood burner in the den and were lazing around reading. Suddenly, Lee got up and went out and it was a while before he returned when, without saying anything, he just settled back down to reading. What was going on? I waited a while before getting up and going through to the kitchen to put the kettle on. I sneaked out the back door, across to the open workshop, straight to the magazine I had found before. Sure enough, there was a new story.

Instantly furious, I snatched up the papers, stalked straight back to the house, straight into the den and waved them at him, demanding, 'What's this? You're supposed to have stopped doing this stuff.'

He looked up and then recognising what I was holding, retorted, 'I've only just written that!' sparking with indignation.

'So what, you're not supposed to be doing any of it,' I flung back. He shrugged, said nothing further and returned to his book. There was no point in pursuing it, so I went back out to make the abandoned tea. I didn't return the story to him, and I reproduce it below, without his various crossings out and alterations. It speaks for itself, so no further comments are necessary.

Carlingwark

As a parlour maid in 1890s England, Mary was privileged to wear a uniform. She was very proud of the jet-black woollen dress that tightly moulded the upper half of her lithe eighteen-year-old body. The neckline was alarmingly low-cut, but she felt no need to worry too much, as her white pinafore concealed her developing bosom. The dress gathered under her full, round breasts, holding and shaping them. From there descended a flowing ankle-length skirt below with polished black shoes and wool socks covering her busy feet. She wore no underwear, as was the custom amongst the serving class of the day. Besides, Mr John would never countenance the wearing of undergarments. Mary smoothed her starched pinafore down the front of her body and carefully finished setting the breakfast table. It was 6.30 am and Mr John would be down soon to conduct the morning session. Each Friday, the household staff was held to account for their transgressions of house rules, neglect of duties or at the mere whim of the master. Ordinarily, this would have been of little concern to Mary, as the discipline of the household was accepted as a fact of life. Discipline at Carlingwark, as at many houses, was meted out via rod and whip applied to soft female skin. This morning, the housekeeper Mrs Bradley had instructed Mary to attend despite not marked down for correction. Apprehension furrowing her brow, she laid out the silver and checked everything was in order; fussing with the bowl of fruit to take her mind off things.

"Ah, young Mary, come here."

"Oh," Mary exclaimed in surprise, as she had not heard the master enter. The familiar anxiety surged through her veins, a mixture of fear and respect.

"Did you hear me? I said come here," he repeated.

"Oh, yes, sir. I'm sorry, sir," she said, hurrying to stand before him, eyes downcast.

Mr John lifted his coattails, letting the fire warm his legs as he looked at the girl. He hadn't really noticed her until recently when she seemed to blossom as a woman. Her long black hair, neatly held in a ribbon, made her complexion seem pale, her green eyes more intense when she glanced furtively at him. He reached out and lifted her chin.

"Remove your pinafore."

"Yes, sir," she said, reaching behind to release the bow and lift it over her head.

"What shall I do with it, sir?"

"Please put it on one of the dining chairs."

He watched as she turned and folded her white apron tidily over a chair back before turning once more to face him. His gaze moved down to her breasts, now barely concealed by the low-cut neckline of her dress, their pale softness entranced him.

"You are a fine looking girl, Mary, and I have decided to take you as my bed companion."

Mary's mind was a whirl, unable to smother her rising blush. She looked down at her hands, twisting her fingers nervously together.

"Mrs Bradley will explain it all to you. I should point out that it will not excuse you from the rod. Quite the opposite, I'm afraid. I forsee a more rigid regime of discipline for you, Mary. A period of training, which I will supervise personally."

"Yes, sir," she mumbled, still afraid to look directly at him.

"You will assist me with punishing Kate, then report to Mrs Bradley, do you understand?"

"Yes, sir."

"Good, arrange a chair for the errant girl, she will need to sit down, and fetch a short strap."

"Yes, sir," she mumbled, grateful to have an excuse to escape. She pulled out a chair as the scullerymaid knocked and entered. Kate was a thin redhead of fifteen and the only candidate for correction that morning. Only minor errors were dealt with on a Friday morning, many of which were of an inconsequential nature. Kate unfortunately had failed to clean some brassware to Mrs Bradley's satisfaction and was here to pay for her dereliction of duty.

"Sit on the chair." Mr John indicated that she should sit on the forward edge of the seat. He lectured her on her failure before announcing the sentence.

"Since your hands are at fault, so shall they take your punishment? Lift her dress, Mary."

The drill was well known to the girls. Kate's dress was gathered up and pulled behind her to rest on the seat of the chair, baring her thighs. She was made to part her legs, displaying her wispy golden mound for all to see before placing her hands, palm up, onto the very top of each leg.

"One on each side, Kate – long," he says. A low moan escapes the girl's mouth, as she knows from bitter experience that long strokes will mark the tender insides of her thighs as well as her soft hands.

The master lifted the strap and hit her hard, the tail of the strap reaching down the inside of her left thigh, imparting its sharp sting. The girl yelped, closed her legs, her eyes screwed shut as she sucked air through her teeth. She opened her legs quickly, not wishing to anger the master, and received the second stroke, the mirror of the first on her other leg. This time she cried out, a short sharp groan, rubbing her thighs together to suppress the pain. Both palms throbbed, both legs bore a red band near their tops.

"Good. Now, back to work, Kate, and attend to your duties more carefully," he admonished.

"Now, Mary, you sit here," he said, indicating the same chair, "and prepare yourself the same way." Raising her skirts behind, Mary placed her buttocks on the front edge of the seat, then gathered her skirts tidily up, sliding the hem up over her knees and along her smooth legs to expose her soft thighs, much as Kate had done. Satisfied that the dress would not impede her correction, she placed her hands palms up. Master John's fingers touched her knee and she obediently parted her thighs as she had been taught. She gazed downwards at the centre of her femininity and waited. His fingers moved along the inside of her leg, testing the soft smoothness. She started to tremble a little then gasped quietly as the fingers reached her sex, brushing lightly over the sparse hair. She sucked air through her teeth and held her breath, fearful of breaking the spell.

"Are you courageous, Mary?"

"Yes, sir, I try to be."

"Will you be brave for me? I will require your total obedience, nothing less."

"I will do as you please, sir."

"Even if I were to tell you that I wish to whip you now, this morning, for my own amusement?"

"If it pleases you, sir, I will try to be brave."

He reached out to lift her chin and looked into her eyes. "That pleases me greatly, my little one, and we shall test that resolve shortly. Go now, find Mrs Bradley and ask her to prepare you. You are to join the training school. You will find a new life there."

Over breakfast, he decided the omens were good.

Rachael. So the liminal space has eased into a decision to sell the house. You seem to be using the garden as your way of coping and looking after yourself. I'm sure you derived a great deal of solace from the natural world of garden and water.

Sheena. Yes, working outside took me out of myself, gave me perspective. Plants are living things, so I wanted to care for them. Nurturing is important for me and is my equivalent of the mothering feelings that most women have.

R. Yes, exactly. Now, you are getting the house ready to go on the market, but a familiar theme is emerging. The idea of duplicity, the surface hiding what is below. Neither of you seem willing to have an open discussion about the future. As you wrote, what happens if you find a suitable house? Would that bring things to a head?

S. Yes, it bothered me a lot, because I couldn't believe he expected us to stay together. Was it naïvety or a clever game or what?

R. It could just be he was miserable and didn't know what to do.

Trapped by pride possibly, not wanting to admit how vulnerable he felt.

S. And at the time, I didn't appreciate what was happening. Too wound up in my own misery and not thinking enough of him.

R. Please, no blame, remember. I'm wondering why you couldn't discuss this though. After all, it was a comparatively safe subject compared with the alternatives. What would have happened if you had?

S. I was afraid. I no longer knew him and certainly didn't trust him. Lee had never been violent at all, but I was afraid of a shouting match, leaving me living with him until the house sold. Everything was so unpredictable and volatile.

R. Can we look briefly at the scene in the kitchen. The description of silence gives a very clear demonstration of how things had deteriorated. As you say, not to show any recognition that someone has sat down and spoken to you is incredibly hard to do. I suggest you have to work at that to overcome instinctive responses; it shows extreme self-control.

S. I'm sure I couldn't. It was so unnerving and very powerful. I just had to leave the room.

R. Let's turn to the business of the belt. This is interesting, as it could have been pleasantly stimulating, a form of stroking. Using a belt rather than fingers creates a different potential, one not so pleasant, and that was the theme of his scenarios. It is the anticipation of what could happen, with the person in control, determining what happens.

S. Yes, to start with, it was playful but then changed to become hurtful, hard enough to sting. The difference between something being pleasurable and turning abruptly to pain. It didn't take much to tip me over to rejection.

R. Are we talking about risk-taking here, the nature of it? Being right on the edge between safe and unsafe is a powerful attraction; for example, to sports people, mountaineers, skydivers and so on. Risk is the thrill of the unknown, being right on the margin of not knowing. In sex games, this creates a delicious uncertainty, will there or won't there be pain? That theme is in the 'Carlingwark' story with different connotations, but we'll come back to that.

S. I see that in sexual activities, risk could be very exciting. There's an exquisite and dangerous line between pain and pleasure, between civilisation and naked dominance. I get a visceral response but can't imagine wanting to be part of it physically. I couldn't trust anyone enough.

R. Everyone has to set their own limits on what they're prepared to do. No rights or wrongs, but most definitely consent. And then, you say, there was the biting. A throwaway line. Clients often use these at the end of a session to indicate unease about disclosing something.

S. You know, I do this quite often. Particularly if I've been talking about something intensely personal.

R. It's a coping device against uncomfortable thoughts or subjects. We needed the information within the narratives, but I wonder if they served a distractive purpose too. Diversionary tactics are common, like the stage magician with his sleight of hand, or in this case, a sleight of mind. Anyway, when did the biting start, are you ready to explore that?

S. It started before the time of the first narrative. Lee had always enjoyed kissing and stroking my breasts, mouthing and nibbling while balancing on the cusp between arousal and discomfort. He then started nipping with his teeth, which made me increasingly uneasy. The skin was never broken, but the marks lasted a few hours. It's a very sensitive area, and after I stopped him, he would agree to nip less hard. He broke that agreement repeatedly, leaving me tense with the expectation of pain. I didn't take the initiative to sort out what was happening but kept putting it off, solving the problem by avoiding sex. I had several other distractions at that time. I was conducting a survey about small businesses and went to meetings all over the region. Needing more academic stimulation, I enrolled on a course studying Scottish history. It opened up many doors for curiosity, which I shared with Lee until he said he was fed up with hearing about it.

R. This is getting serious, as he is physically hurting you against your specific request. Does he feel you are drifting away from him and this is a punishment? Or is he trying to introduce more variety and buzz into your sex life? Either way, you retreat further. By this time, you are looking for other stimuli, other interests, which maybe he interpreted as you turning away from him.

S. Possibly. I wasn't looking at my actions in any logical way at that point. The biting wasn't pleasant, so it's good to talk about it.

R. I'm glad you could, not an easy subject to confide. Turning now to the stories. In addition to arousal, Lee used these to find relief and soothing from his anxieties, as we have discussed before regarding porn. The body of anyone experiencing erotica, or other pleasure-seeking activity, releases dopamine, a chemical substance, enabling them to experience reward and pleasure. We mentioned this before in connection to the effects of porn. There is a hooked effect as the brain develops a bias towards activities giving that same reward. Anticipation of pleasure and fantasy heighten the dopamine levels, but over time, more is needed to get the same high.

S. Could that explain the progression from porn to stories?

R. Possibly, but there is another element. Sometimes people cannot produce sufficient dopamine themselves and turn to external sources to make up the difference, hence the stories. It is an escape manoeuvre, to live temporarily in a fantasy world that they control. It is more to do with survival than pleasure. Now, we all have fantasies and daydreams, think of the Mills and Boon stories; woman dreams of a handsome, wealthy man sweeping her off her feet. People have fantasies about holidays, bigger houses, winning prizes, etc. We need daydreams to give ourselves strokes of praise, to be lauded, but they have two closely related themes, wealth and power. These are particularly pertinent for sexual-based fantasies. The content of Lee's stories is about power and the wealthy exercising dominance; living within that fantasy is very empowering.

Let's turn now to the tying up incident, which was sometime before the belt story. I can appreciate why you reacted, as it came with no warning. Lee probably found the idea exciting and I imagine he wasn't expecting you to behave as you did.

S. I think he realised he'd gone too far.

R. We have a theme here, haven't we; bondage, dominance, submission, S and M. These themes didn't suddenly appear, they have been under the surface for sometime with occasional excursions, like this one. All these activities come under the heading 'kinky', which is an accepted legitimate genre. Those who practice kinky behaviour have the slogan 'safe, sane and consensual' with the crucial word being consent, freely given. Otherwise it's abuse. Kinky is about games and fun, not the control, forced submission and punishments of the erotic fantasies.

So let's look at the first story. The wife admits wrongdoing and the need to be punished. It is unlikely to be genuine consent, as that would remove the purpose of the story. It doesn't suit this, or any of the genre, to have blatant violence. It must be a tightly controlled environment. Control is important to maintain the ritualistic or formulaic aspect, with the rituals creating the formula. We know by the careful, slowly developed storyline in 'Carlingwark' that this was where the source of pleasure lies; the anticipation and excitement, the eroticism heightened by a dopamine high. To a lesser extent, the same reactions were evoked by the porn videos or by studying the details of the escorts written in the diary. This is all about the planning and the journey to the end, normally an orgasm, rather than the end itself.

S. And he planned in real life to, by travelling over to Dundee to see Rosa. It always amazed me how much energy he spent in planning and carrying out those visits. He must have been exhausted.

R. That's a good example. And when you consider that with orgasm, the dopamine dissipates, it makes sense that Lee wanted to spend the night over there, he needed some recovery time. There were rituals with those visits too, as in the wine glasses, Rosa's name badge and the tin they were kept in.

We use rituals to calm us in all kinds of situations; mantras, setting a time for evening drinks, the order of performing domestic tasks. The fantasy rituals serve the same purpose, particularly if they are experienced in your own space. Lee could distant himself from everyday life and enter a fantasy world through the stories.

S. It was like living with two different, quite separate people. When I marched in with that last story, I expect he thought I wanted to control him. It wasn't that, I was just so upset about his secret world; it seemed to be escalating. To me, his fantasy eroticism was more important than sorting out his marriage; the fear of facing himself was greater than his feelings for me. I think he resented that I didn't throw him out, as he was in my debt now. I had been the strong one, yet again, and he couldn't deal with that.

R. I doubt if it's as clear-cut as that. He genuinely had trouble in articulating how he felt, which is why he withdrew. He just couldn't do it. You have that as well to some extent, but that's the way you are, you both are. As we mentioned in a previous session, Lee would find it very hard to change and certainly would need help to do so, but you have a more positive attitude and find change easier. Before we end, can I draw a parallel between the long drawn-out lovemaking of the Cad sequence and 'Carling-wark'. Very different scenarios, but the same journeying theme. If you think about it, much of our lives is spent in travelling rather than arriving; planning holidays, for instance. Make of that what you will, although it's outside our current scope.

I think that's enough for now, too much to ponder. Let's leave it there.

S. Yes, please. A difficult session, but thank you for today.

Session Nine

Convergence | Narrative

We finished smartening up the house, refreshing paintwork and deep cleaning before putting it on the market. We hadn't discussed where we would go but had an unspoken agreement to rent for a bit, as our house searches hadn't produced anything suitable at an affordable price. I used my business contacts to find somewhere, using the house sale as an excuse for needing temporary accommodation. Some of them would have guessed there was more to it than that, as marital breakups can't be kept quiet in a small community. Eventually, I was offered a cottage owned by one of my business clients. It was set aside for trainee staff on deployment but wouldn't be needed for several months. It was furnished, so most things could go into storage, which suited well, and it had a phone and computer link. We could both move there and I think, initially, Lee assumed that would be the case.

While awaiting viewings, I began shifting through the tea chests in storage under the eaves. Some weeding out had been done before moving to Scotland, but there were still plenty of papers, university notes and essays, poultry catalogues, old diaries, etc; all the detritus of a life, bundled into boxes out of sight. I filled bin bags, reducing the past to one manageable box, and made a stack of other surplus items including a chair, rugs and a couple of pictures. These were too scruffy for a charity shop, so burning was the obvious solution. The cleaning up process produced plenty of material from inside and out, requiring frequent burnings in the area reserved for bonfires. I would get a good blaze going before chucking on with gay abandon, although had momentary regret over one picture. Too late though, it had gone. The flames were cathartic, frightening and fascinating, linking with our primitive past. I remembered my father disappearing down the garden to spend hours with his bonfire, escaping from my mother's nags and moans. Meanwhile, the house attracted plenty of interest due to its location, keeping us busy with tidying up and discussing each set of viewers. We were surprised by the number and realised it should sell pretty quickly. We adopted the habit of washing up immediately after any meal and clearing up after ourselves throughout the day. Lee was at work during the week, so I tried to be at home for any weekday viewing, although the agents took over when necessary. While that went on, our lives continued in their artificial, contrived way. On the surface, all was as usual, but you didn't have to scratch very far to find the falsity, the illusion.

It was a strange time and one night in particular illustrated that. I could not settle to sleep, despite my mind having no new thoughts to churn. There was an emptiness but no calm as I lay awake in the dark; not complete dark, as there was a full moon glimmering through the open curtains. There were no man-made lights; the trees in full leaf hid the flashing buoy on the estuary. Lying there, I became aware of a small noise near the ceiling and questioned what it was. Then I realised it was the moth that earlier had bumped around the bedside lampshade on my side of the bed. Dicing with death like Icarus but surviving for another day. Now the light was off, it was still fluttering around and I imagined it looking down on the two shapes in the bed, just discernible in the soft light. What was it like to look down from the ceiling onto the bed? There are reports of people leaving their bodies behind and looking down on themselves, a close encounter with death or chemically induced. The moth had the same viewpoint. I mused on the possibility of telling the health of a relationship from the position of the shapes in the bed. I suspected that most of the time, for most couples, there would be a physical distance between them. After all, both partners would want some space of their own, so they could shift from side to side without disturbance. A companionable space would be left between or a distance of indifference; we didn't come into either of those categories. I turned away from Lee, perched on the edge, precariously balanced while keeping the maximum gap. He faced away from me, with knees slightly bent as normal. There can be few lonelier places than a double bed containing two people not getting on. Nights of hunched up misery and a damp pillow with tentative fingers reaching out to the tissue box. I thought back to not long ago, when we lay close, not touching but close, a mere stretch of the fingers encountering another's skin. It gave the possibility of a quick touch of connection, of reassurance that neither of us was alone. Or the times of post-coital entwinement when we fell asleep, waking later for gentle disentanglement before falling back asleep.

I realised I was using the moth musings as a distraction, almost a mantra, to take me away off the treadmill of tears, take me from further imaginings of Lee's exploits. I created another distraction and drifted further back, away from the present to our uncomplicated life as students. Back to our early sexual encounters of sharing a single bed in each other's rooms, in our respective halls of residence. I became very adept at wedging in the gap between wall and bed, judged wide enough to accommodate half of me but narrow enough to prevent capsizing onto the floor. The sheets being well tucked in for additional security. I smiled at those memories of simple pleasures while being calmed into sleep.

Other times, going out was an escape from enduring an evening in the same house with carefully orchestrated avoidance. Increasingly, we were drinking wine with every main meal and whereas previously, one glass each would have been sufficient, now we finished a whole bottle. On one particular evening, there was a birthday celebration for an acquaintance we knew from the local pub. Lee wouldn't have bothered normally, but I think we were both grateful for an excuse to be with other people. I had pottered outside during the day while Lee had been tidying the workshop. We had not been together at all, as he had had a lunchtime sandwich at his bench. It felt I was going out with a stranger, only coming together for the sake of the party. I went into the house and upstairs for a shower and clean up, taking time to enjoy the chance of relaxing under the water.

Back in the bedroom, I needed to change into clean clothes and took out two pairs of jeans, unsure which to wear. The whole situation was affecting me, to the point I had difficulty choosing which jeans, fawn or dark blue. I laid them out on the bed, deliberating, while I stood in my underwear, my back to the doorway. I became aware of Lee coming up the stairs and assumed he was going to change too. I didn't turn round as I heard him walk into the bedroom behind me. I sensed him coming closer. He placed his hands each side of my hips. 'Get these off,' he demanded, low and urgent in my ear while pulling my knickers down. Surprise made for obedience. His hands moved to my shoulders. 'Kneel on the bed,' came the next command, and again I complied. This doggy position was not uncommon for us. It often served as a playful introduction to more caring, prolonged coupling. Today was different, there was no warmth, no caring, the balance had been upset; the trust destroyed and the bond severed. 'Her' below didn't realise this, did not discriminate. I could feel her moistness while 'her' in my head was stunned, disorientated. One hand still on my shoulder, he entered me without ceremony. I could not imagine this taking long; seconds, not the minutes we used to share. I just wanted it over. I felt so helpless; I was being taken, being used. My submission had joined me to that long ribbon of women encircling the room, out of the window and down, down over the horizon of history. The warmth of being desired had been replaced by the chill of being used. His breathing quickened and with a final exhalation, he had finished. He withdrew and without a word disappeared to the bathroom, leaving his semen, cooling and viscous, to trickle down my legs and puddle on the sheet. I was numbed into silence, my mind switched off, as it knew protest was pointless. So much for modern women and the body under the horse's hooves at the Epsom Derby. I had been reduced to this, me, by no means a virgin but still despoiled. And the question I asked as the tears fell, 'Why, why on earth did I allow that to happen, that consensual rape?'

I waited until I heard him come out of the bathroom and go downstairs. I picked my jeans up, first pair I came to, no worries about colour, and cleaned myself up. Clean seemed an inappropriate word, as if soap could ever cleanse. I went back down and into the kitchen still feeling dazed. Lee unhooked his denim jacket off the back of a chair and moved towards the door. 'Ready?' he asked, and without waiting for an answer, headed out the door. I followed wordlessly and we made our way down the hill to the pub in silence. Fortunately, we met up with another couple we knew heading for the same party, so the normal business of polite exchanges helped to settle us back into an approximation of normality. At the pub, all was lively and cheerful, but we left well before the end. Once home, I went to the spare room and closed the door. No apology or explanation was made then or later.

Convergence | Therapy

Rachael. We are now at the ninth narrative out of a total of ten, and I imagine the tenth will be more of a winding up. Along the way, we have had several dramatic events, but I don't think any of them match the one you give here. The effect was intensified by the contrast with the moth musing, miserable but peaceful, and the other, a travesty of normal. A truly awful experience. Thank you for being prepared to talk about it and engage in exploring the consequences.

Sheena. It has left a legacy that I should like to explore further, to get some understanding of why I was so compliant.

R. Yes, we can do that. The existing situation was difficult already and I liked the way you used the moth to bring out, very clearly, the loneliness of that period. By focusing on a particular night, one of many, you brought home what a miserable time it was.

S. I used to retreat to the spare room occasionally, but he hated that. I suppose, looking back, it emphasised in a very poignant way how alone he felt.

R. Yes, I think so. We'll look at the rape question in more detail shortly. First, though, can I say I am intrigued that it's not until the eighth narrative that you mentioned tying up and biting. The previous narratives seemingly acting, in part, as a diversion, a defence.

S. Yes, I wasn't aware before, but now see it was a defence, against having to acknowledge the other side of the man I thought I knew. I'd kept it all buried back then but have now reached a point of finally facing it. Realising that Lee's fantasy world had steadily encroached on our lives.

R. Well done, that's a major turning point in your understanding. Your next revelation is the most serious one, the marital rape, although it is interesting that you use the term 'consensual rape'. At first glance, this is a contradiction in terms; by definition, rape can never be consensual. I sense you used that phase deliberately to convey the impact it had.

S. Yes, it was a form of assault, so felt like rape, but consensual as I didn't say no, I didn't push him away. I acquiesced, was just compliant.

R. Unsure about your logic here. Not saying no does not automatically equal consent. It is clear that this was not consensual. You are blaming yourself, despairing at yourself, but one thing appears to be missing, and that's anger. Why, do you think?

S. I don't know. You're right. I wasn't angry. It was all very bleak, as I say in the piece. If what happened had been entirely all his fault, I might have felt angry. Except I wasn't innocent, as I had contributed to some extent, I couldn't pretend otherwise.

R. And that means you're not allowed to be angry, in your eyes? We've talked previously about this and I think we agreed that, whatever the contribution you may have made, it did not excuse Lee's behaviour or the extent of his deceit. And it certainly does not excuse this episode whatsoever. I'm wondering how much difference it would have made if this had been a stranger or someone you didn't know very well. Would you have been compliant then?

S. Oh no! If someone comes up behind me unexpectedly and touches me, my immediate reaction is to recoil. Can be a bit embarrassing if someone is only touching me to get my attention, but I've learned to manage that. Anything intimate, as in this situation, I would react aggressively, instinctively.

R. Mmmm, I'm just remembering the tying up episode, where you did react aggressively. So what was the difference here?

S. It was as if my reactions had been suspended. There's fight and flight, but the third one is freeze and that's what I did. Birds and animals use that as defence don't they? I think there's some weird logic here. If I reacted, I would have to acknowledge I didn't want to be there. And then what? What was I going to do about it? Be more helpless than I was already? But I didn't feel, at least not with my head, just received, without any processing, just took what was coming. How did I let him do that?

R. A bit convoluted, but I think I understand what you're saying. Perhaps there is resignation here, that you know your relationship is nearing an end but not fully conscious of it yet. It's also echoing the situation back in session two when you found the hotel receipt. What happens if I challenge? Acceptance as opposed to confrontation. There is no excuse for what happened though. It was a massive shock, completely unexpected. This was someone you knew and trusted, so there was no sense of danger. Admittedly, that trust had become eroded, but there was no reason to expect an assault like this. And it was an assault, it was marital rape.

S. Yes, I suppose so. Actually, it helps to give it a label. Despite all the time elapsed, I haven't told anyone before. Not sure why. But the fact remains, I didn't say no... People tell me I can be a feisty woman, but certainly not then. Education and intelligence are for nothing, and it makes you wonder if women have achieved anything; the veneer of feminism so paper thin, so easily ripped, revealing primeval submission. Women are left mentally stunned, ready to accept whatever the male wants to take. It is not pretty. We are still bearing the burden of generations from time immemorial.

R. Disillusioned or reality? It is perfectly understandable that the experience had a longstanding impact on you. I would say justified. I hope that finally telling the story has helped ease the memory. The idea of the generational role of women and their expectations is a powerful image. There are still so many injustices and misconceptions. Let's not forget that the law was on the men's side until relatively recently. In Scotland, it was not until 1989 that marital rape finally became illegal, with England a few years behind. In fact, the idea of a husband raping his wife was regarded as nonsensical, impossible even, as he was entitled to have sex regardless of her wishes. It makes a mockery of the whole concept of making love. Let's widen this out a bit. Rape is more than a sexual act, an invasion. It can be viewed as a desecration of the soul; the ultimate symbol for taking the soul, which is why it's used as a weapon by soldiers of invading armies. It could be useful to consider the wider implications for you. You experienced the loss of your best friend, your pal of many years, and now he had destroyed any remaining bond of goodwill. You have to fall back on your own resources once more.

S. Yes, I think that's true. I had to replay the 'alone' situation over again and find a new way forward. The person I believed had loved me for myself, over many years, no longer existed. He had destroyed any vestiges of the belief I once held. We're back to the mother question, aren't we? I suppose in a way, she tried to take my soul by trying to mould me into what she wanted.

R. Almost a form of mental rape, that's an interesting idea. For you, the physical act of this rape had other repercussions, as it brought back up to the surface all the uncertainties and doubts we have mentioned before. About whom you can trust.

S. Yes, definitely. Also, I think it illustrated how far Lee had split one world from another. He disappeared into burrows like his workshops and the hotel rooms, for instance. He had a fantastical make-believe world that was reduced to tawdry banality when he emerged into daylight.

R. I agree. There are two realities, the everyday one, on the surface, getting along together, sometimes OK, but sometimes very much not OK. Then we have Lee with his personal fantasy world, his stories, videos and the escorts who are real people but acting out a fantasy for him. Now, though, I am gradually seeing how the two realities are moving together with a dreadful aura of inevitability. Perhaps that theme was there right at the beginning, but we were not aware then. There is convergence, so let's try together to trace what is happening, by going back to the Glasgow interlude. Although other discoveries have been made, Rosa remains lurking in the background. She won't go away, possibly because she's named, you've seen her website photo; she is more tangible than the others. Rosa represents that world of fantasy, but now she's drawn into the reality of you and Lee in the pub.

S. Yes, of course. I hadn't thought of it like that. And also, in her photo, she is dressed up as if playing a part, another aspect of the make-believe.

R. So, the two worlds are converging, which they haven't done before in this stark way, hovering but not converging. The scene of marital rape is irrefutably fantasy and reality clashing together and melding. Goodness knows what was going through his mind when that was going on, you in your underwear setting him off maybe. This is the sort of action he recounts in his writings; availability of women, sex on demand, no questions asked. In the fantasies, there isn't overt violence, but a man is getting what he wants; if he wants sex, he has sex. There is no scope for a woman to object; she just has to accept it. Apparently, this was what Lee was acting out with you.

S. It's all so sad though, isn't it? Sad because it's rather pathetic and unnecessary. He wasn't interested in getting any sort of help. I concluded that his fear of confronting whatever demons he had was greater than his love for me. In other words, I came second and I found that difficult to come to terms with.

R. I very much doubt he articulated anything like that. He had retreated to feeling alone, hence the descent into the fantasy world.

S. He said once, 'I've never felt so alone.'

R. No doubt, but he doesn't go on to say, 'It doesn't have to be like this.' He or both of you could have got help. Invariably, that would have involved making changes at some level. As I've said previously, a person has to be actively receptive to the idea of changing. It cannot be imposed. And of course, you both have a long history of not talking about how you feel, of being self-reliant, which drove you further and further apart. I think he did love you very much but despaired at what to do.

S. I've been mulling over those narratives a lot. There were other factors involved, but sex is acting as a symbol or metaphor. I understand now, although not at the time, that Lee was getting bored with our sex life; it was more sex than making love. He tried to introduce new things by imposition, not negotiation, so not surprisingly, I rejected them. I should have taken more notice, tried to do something new. Maybe that would've made a difference.

R. I think you're right that sex was symbolic and the emphasis was on that part of your lives. If anyone's sex life is getting a bit stale, there are all sorts of ways to invigorate it. No matter the method – new positions, sex toys, licking chocolate in navels, whatever – it has to be consensual, the rules agreed between you and trust they will be kept. You both have to enjoy it, otherwise what's the point? Otherwise, it can descend into abuse. Basically,

Lee was doing that with you. It was not consensual, it was a form of abuse. I'm sure there are people who would dismiss that as nonsense, but it's not; psychologically, it was abuse and that's what matters.

S. Even so, I have to face the fact I'm not adventurous in trying new techniques. In the narrative about my sexual history, it was obvious I enjoyed making love but not necessarily sex. I needed a safe territory. I suppose I shy away from the earthier aspects and prefer the aesthetic. We used to enjoy differing locations and sensations from the classic deep rug by the fire to a bed of crushed clover, cool on a summer night. That must have got too tame for him and it makes me out to be a prissy prude. However, if I did indulge in more robust stuff, I would fear losing control, and if that happened, I could lose myself. Would be like lifting the corner of my security blanket and letting cold air in. Which takes us straight back to narrative one, doesn't it? The legacy we carry throughout life.

R. Although you were happy to explore different partners, you're reluctant to be tempted out to riskier shores. So what? You do what's right for you. We all have our likes and dislikes that need to be respected. No good doing things we don't want to – back to consent again. We can be persuaded to try something out of the normal, that's true of anything; eating an unusual food, for example. A gradual introduction to allow time to get used to it, if at all. Lee was not persuading but imposing. Anyway, as I have said before, the fantasy world is not about sex, it is all to do with self-soothing. I should like to change the subject slightly and talk briefly about honesty. Trust implies couples are honest with each other and that is pertinent here. A demand for complete honesty would be controlling and unrealistic, as each person needs their own private world. There are things you would not want anyone else, including your partner, to know about. The crucial question is, would it be a serious threat to your marriage if those secrets were exposed? On starting a relationship, we don't stop being two individuals but rather add a third component, the couple. Ideally all three parts are equally balanced so individual autonomy is maintained without threatening the couple element. Your relationship with Lee had become out of balance regarding the two of you separately and the two of you as a couple.

S. Out of sync. We weren't to start with, but the imbalance had crept up on us without either noticing.

R. Yes, that sounds right. I think you'd helped him to put the demons aside for many years while you were together. Unfortunately, they were waiting to rear their ugly heads when he faced a serious challenge, hence the escalation. I should like to move from there and go back to the rape. I'm conscious of you saying you had not told anyone about it before. I hope that telling has helped lessen the emotional impact.

S. Writing about it had an interesting effect. When I started thinking about that event, recalling what had happened, I became very upset. Gradually as I started writing, remembering more detail and then editing the writing, the emotional response settled down. It was all still there as a vivid memory but with fewer tears and less melancholia. Writing had a liberating effect and allowed me to face a very uncomfortable truth. After all this time, it is possible for me to accept that I was abused. I let it all happen and the rape was the last in a series of escalating acts.

Sorry, that's another throwaway line.

R. Let's pause there; you've just made a major revelation that is likely to resonate with you for a long time. It's outside the scope of our work here and we have only one more session left. Please take time to reflect and consider what you'd like to do, but you are welcome to come back to work through this further. Or somewhere else, of course, but I do feel further work would be helpful for you.

S. It's only now it has occurred to me that it could be abuse. I think it would be good to work on the impact of that realisation, to come to terms with it. Thank you for offering, I'd like to come back.

Session Ten

Culmination | Narrative

THIS WAS A TIME OF hurtling towards the inevitable conclusion. Several people had expressed a serious interest in the house and three had made offers. We now had the task of judging who was the most reliable in terms of producing the required cash. All this juggling and negotiating took time and proved very frustrating. Finally, a sale was agreed and the agony of waiting was replaced by the urgency of packing and sorting. The removal firm delivered a small mountain of tea chests and cardboard boxes for us to start packing. Keeping the place tidy no longer mattered, so we could spread boxes out in each room. I attempted to pack personal items that clearly belonged to one or other of us in separate boxes. The obvious category was books, but they were too heavy to fill more than half a tea chest, so cushions and soft stuff made up the space. It was inevitable that going through the tangible belongings of a life together would be painful and produce bouts of nostalgia; I was packing the boxes with memories. I thought of all the time, energy and belief that had created this house and garden and that naturally lead back to previous homes.

I wandered around the garden, taking cuttings and splitting without removing the whole plant. Moving to a rented house restricted how many plants I could take, but anything in pots could come with us. I felt myself make a tentative mental shift, as though nostalgia for our life behind was morphing into optimism about the challenge ahead. Was this my basic problem, needing new challenges, new changes? All through that time, the question of parting hovered, never asked, never voiced, but understood. The day came when there was no hiding the truth. Our lawyer visited to go over the final papers for the sale and get our signatures. He knew we each had our own bank accounts, so he asked into which account to transfer the sale proceeds. I took a deep breath before asking him to split the money equally between us. He didn't need an explanation, but his face was a picture. After a few seconds, he said, 'Right, it's like that is it?'

'Yes,' I replied.

He said he was sorry to hear it, as he had known us for many years, but took it in his stride, as lawyers tend to do. Lee didn't show any surprise, realising the inevitability of it. After the paperwork was completed and the lawyer left, there was no discussion. Lee simply said he would find somewhere to stay. A few days later, he came home and announced he'd been offered a cottage on the Druids estate, already furnished as a holiday let. I thought that an excellent solution, although it meant he had to tell the Druids staff what was happening. I imagine he would have liked to keep it quiet for a bit longer. The other people needing to be told at some point were our respective mothers. I had not mentioned any of our problems to my mother, as I couldn't face all the inevitable recriminations. The last thing she would be was supportive. She would expect me to put up with whatever was happening and there would be an 'I told you so' in the mix. If she had known anything of the truth, she would have blamed both of us, but I saw no reason to reveal that. Lee seldom spoke to his mother and he offered to delay telling her until I felt able to tell mine. I was immensely grateful for that, but he knew how difficult my mother could be. It was one major source of stress postponed. On the practical front, I could transfer our landline number to the rented cottage, so she needn't know I had moved.

The day came and the removal men arrived. There was one large lorry for stuff going into storage and two small vans, one going to Dumfries for Lee and one to Kirkcudbright for me. After a while, I went upstairs and looked out of the window down onto the driveway. The removal lorry stood there, almost full now, with one of the men leaning against the side, pouring from a thermos. Lee was showing the other man the bits in the workshop that were going with him. I looked down by the front door. There were two groups of plant pots, the bigger ones, including a big blue urn that couldn't fit in a car, were going with me while the smaller ones were to be split between us. I stared down at them, appalled. Had it really all come down to this? Twenty-six years together reduced to groups of plant pots waiting to go their separate ways.

I turned from the window and wandered around the empty rooms upstairs, checking nothing had been missed. I went into the main bedroom. Here we had shared a bed, slept together in the sexual sense and the plain literal sense. Here I had perched on the edge of the bed as far away from him without actually falling onto the floor. Here where I had let the tears wet the pillow night after night in silence. Here I had kept things going, holding back, waiting for all the arrangements to be in place, not wanting to rock the boat. Here I had cried with him, hoping he would change. He hated me going into the spare room, but sometimes I needed to. I went back downstairs to check the rooms. Here in the dining room he had so carefully planned and created, we had had some wonderful meals. Christmas lunches that we had produced together. All the best pottery and the silver cutlery, the table decorated and the candles lit. The meal prepared with care and served up with joy. Where was that now? How could it have become so tarnished and so debased? Here in the kitchen, I remembered the times he came back from work, sat down at the table and sipped his tea in silence.

Now, the furniture and boxes were all on the lorry, including the bed and the kitchen chairs, while the two vans had received their loads. I went round the house doing a final check for emptiness, but even the spiders had tidied themselves away. I had removed the last cobweb to leave the place bare, just the light bulbs hanging exposed and a curtain or two no longer required. I said to the van men, 'That's it, that's the lot,' and they echoed, 'Yes, that's all.' I got into my car, settled Beth on the seat beside me, unable to speak, the tears poised to fall. Lee came up to the window, knocked on the glass. I opened it slightly. He stood there, an anxious lonely face.

'Goodbye then,' he said and raised his hand.

'Goodbye,' I managed and drove away, leaving him standing there. Of course, we would meet to sort out arrangements, but this was goodbye to the home and life we had shared. It was time to move on, away from deceit and lies. James Grant accompanied me along the road to my cottage, asking me, 'Does it all add up to nothing?' At that point, I think it did.

* * *

A continental market is filling the pedestrianised centre of Dumfries and Jane and I are sitting outside a café in the early autumn sun, warm but with a hint of a coolness to come. We have just visited the ATM to top up resources and are enjoying a coffee before the next onslaught. Jane and Robert are making some major changes to their house and Jane is looking out for bits and pieces from the stalls. She looks over to me and asks, 'How long is it now?'

'Six weeks.'

'And how long did it last?'

'Twenty-six years.'

'That's a long time, you wouldn't think it would end after all that time.'

'That's the illusion.'

'Mmm, I suppose.'

'Or the delusion, but I am not going to sit around moping.'

'What? You're looking for another man?'

'No way, absolutely not. No more men.'

'Huh.'

'Anyway, I have made a move into my new life. I have booked a holiday for next year. Sailing round the Hebrides in a classic wooden sailing boat. Something we had considered before but never got round to. So, I'm going to do it on my own. Anyway, what are credit cards for?'

'Wow, good for you, why not!'

And on that positive note, we continue our shopping.

Culmination | Therapy

Rachael. So, we come to the end, the old cliché of sailing off into the sunset, and it is satisfying, from my point of view, that you have given a glimpse of what lay over that horizon. I'm glad that you had made plans for the holiday, showing optimism and hope for the future. However, all these stories are about the events of, what, nine years ago now? Although it is not in our remit, just to satisfy my own curiosity, am I allowed to know what has happened since?

Sheena. Yes, of course. After the breakup, we both rented for a while before buying new properties and Lee found someone else fairly quickly. It seems men, generally speaking, find it difficult to be on their own. I don't know how they met, internet possibly, as she lived near Edinburgh. Eventually, he found a job up there and moved to be with her. I haven't heard whether they are still together, as we lost contact after the sorting out of belongings and the divorce was completed. And I, well, eventually, I have found someone else too. We met shortly before I joined this project. He lives up in Ayrshire, so not far away, and we are both in our early seventies. There is no question of living together, but we meet up frequently, go to social things with mutual friends, go away for weekends and holidays and it works very well. All the pluses without the negatives, a sort of companions with cuddles arrangement. Sadly, the one tragedy was Beth. She developed tumours and had to be put down. She wasn't that young at the time I was writing, but three years later, she had gone. I couldn't be without a dog, so after a decent interval, I got a teenage rough-coated Jack Russell bitch called Jen. And I took another course, at this university, on local history – Balliol, Covenanters, John Paul Jones, the lot.

R. And not forgetting the Bard, I hope. That's really positive. I'm so glad you have made a new life for yourself and things have turned out well despite the burden of memories.

S. One thing that horrifies me is how long it took to get some counselling and start working through things. Fortunately, I heard about this research project and decided to apply. It has definitely helped to lay things to rest, finally, so thank you.

R. I'm very pleased to hear that. Now, let's continue summing up. Remember we talked before about your losses being a form of bereavement. Although no one had actually died, there were major losses that had the same effect. You lost your relationship, a way of life, your pal, your best friend and then you lost your home. In conventional bereavement, people don't just get over it, as it's not a question of forgetting and putting it behind you. While at first the impact of losses is with you all the time, gradually it grows fainter, although never forgotten. It becomes possible to continue with life without allowing loss and sadness to infiltrate and undermine you. People talk about moving on from grief, but I think it is more akin to growing on, on and away.

S. The problem is, you think you are continuing with life, but really it's only superficial, as the sadness can rear up and bite you at unexpected moments. It has got a lot easier, although, as you say, never forgotten. I put on a positive front at the shopping trip, but otherwise there was weeping, loneliness and despair. Luckily, my natural optimism prevailed in the end and this therapy has been the final stage of the process.

R. Hopefully, it's now more a case of being alongside the grief, journeying through everyday life with the good memories beside you, giving you strength. There is always the mental memory box to bring out and revisit to help you appreciate the good times. Although sad bits are lurking in the background, they are not having the same influence as before.

S. Yes, that's true. That is happening.

R. So let's now look at how the Narrative Memoir Therapy method worked. As this is a research project, I shall need to present a report based on the observations of both of us. First, let's look at how this method is different from a conventional one. Usually, during counselling, you would tell your story but not necessarily chronologically. Normally you would be talking only, but writing about events can very helpful, and there have been many studies exploring the therapeutic benefits. The form can vary from writing for a few minutes to a longer exercise of the stream of consciousness type. The writing can be at home, with no pressure to share it with anyone else. Now, this method involved writing in an organised, chronological way, which was important, as it gave continuity to the project. Do you think writing gave a different dimension?

S. Yes, I think so. I have had various counselling sessions, as you know from the narratives, and they were just talking. What happened in the writing... it was more than talking, because I had a record on paper. I could go over it, and by reading it again, I was retelling and reliving it. I think that helped, as it made for a concentrated retelling.

R. Yes, a good point, because one of the methods to help people overcome traumatic events is to get them to repeat the telling. This can lessen some of the emotional impact, like a form of exposure lessening the effect. Regarding the method, it would be useful to look at two viewpoints, yours as the client and mine as the therapist. Do you think it was helpful writing all the stories first before the therapy began?

S. A hell of a lot of work, but fortunately I enjoy writing. Could I make the point that five shorter narratives would be less daunting and encourage more participants?

R. Yes, I have mentioned that in my notes. The current method severely limits the opportunities for potential clients. It was a lot to expect from you and we were very lucky you met the challenge.

S. Writing comes easily to me, but that is not true for everyone. I was able to think back and immerse myself in the perspective of the time. Completing all the writing first meant there was no influence from anything said during a session. Otherwise, a bias could be introduced before writing the next narrative.

R. Good point. Similarly, from my point of view, going through the stories one by one meant that I wasn't influenced by later events. This prevented them from causing possible contamination. The overall approach allowed greater focus on a particular event, confining hindsight to therapy in an accumulative way. I would say the method worked very well, from a therapist's point of view. But how was it for you, the participant?

S. Well, obviously I did know what happened, but by voicing it bit by bit, in chunks, I was able to apply myself to a particular episode, like putting on blinkers. They were manageable portions for scrutiny and analysis and made me concentrate on what was happening within a set time capsule. It allowed a gradual dissecting and dismantling of events; the perspective using hindsight. It helped me remember that whatever I did, it was valid at that moment. There was no point blaming in retrospect.

R. Yes, absolutely, another important point. Whatever your reactions, opinions, etc. were, they were valid at that time, as you had no other information at that stage.

S. I think this method provides an honest insight into what was happening.

R. Right, that's the method, but now let's look at how you were helped. To start with, we had the memoir, the narrative from your individual standpoint as events unfolded. We then explored new ways of interpreting what had happened from the perspective of hindsight, making new meanings for why you and Lee behaved the way you did. Rather than be constrained by the perceptions of the time, we opened ourselves to a multiplicity of stories and new interpretations. Is that your experience?

S. Yes, it meant I had a greater appreciation of what happened.

R. Do you think that deep down, unconsciously, you realised you had reached the end, had travelled as far as you could as a couple and now needed to part?

S. Yes, it was unconscious, but I think there were hints breaking through the surface. I didn't realise it then, but looking back, it is much clearer. Makes you aware how blind you can be.

R. That's true for all of us, I'm afraid. There's nothing to say couples have to stay together for life. There is a theory that we need different partners at different stages of life. Could this be what happened here? It worked so well for a long time, but then you needed something different, new challenges. I think we said before, can't remember where, about both of you being on different trajectories. That seems to be the crux of the issue, as you continued upwards while Lee was flatlining. There are no rights or wrongs in that, everyone needs to find their own balance, but the difference caused some fundamental problems for your marriage. His sexual tastes, aberrations, have been there over a long time, building up, and as we have said, he was using them as solace. I suspect he realised you were leaving him, leaving him psychologically in mind and to some extent in body.

S. Yes, I think that's true. It isn't in the narratives, but at one point he said, 'You don't need me anymore.' I didn't understand at the time but do now. He was right. I had become more distant, creating my own life, but wasn't aware of the effect. I was not conscious of what was happening, so not able to articulate it, maybe afraid to face the reality of not wanting to continue. I chose to ease away, making a separate life, which he saw as a threat. I didn't want answers, as I didn't really want to be there. Even if a temporary solution had been found, the fundamental problems would have remained.

R. Yes, I think so. I fear you would have felt trapped after a while and ended up in exactly the same place.

S. Yes, it has been a fascinating process unravelling before my eyes. At times, when I was talking about things I had not told anyone before, I experienced a real physical easing. I realised I had these little bundles inside me that were kept tied up tight – with garden twine, in my imagination – because I didn't want to share them. The therapy sessions loosened those bindings by helping me view them in a different light. I had allowed the situation to develop whereby Lee ended up doing the stuff that he did, doing it to comfort himself. Looking back, I regret that I did not fully understand that he was actually very needy and lonely. I do regret that, because I know what it's like to be alone, and I feel sad that, in a way, I inflicted that on him. But it is gone, it's in the past. I don't do 'if onlys', but I do have a legacy of sadness.

R. You just have to do what you think is right at the time, based on the knowledge you have at the time.

S. If faced with that situation again, highly unlikely, I know, I hope I would be more sensitive, have more understanding of what was required. Going back to those knots and bundles, I feel the hindsight perspective has helped loosen the bindings, some of them completely, others not. The ones about regret, they won't go away; the hurt I caused him unknowingly will always be there, but not in such stark, black and white terms. They have eased and been blended in with everything else, ebbing and flowing inside my head. My perspective now is more balanced, looking forward rather than back. The project has allowed me to reach peace, to give myself absolution, and for that, I am very grateful.

R. A very honest assessment. So, my thanks to you and thank you for working with me on your very personal journey. I feel privileged to have been part of it. To summarise, can we say there are positive outcomes from this method but a drawback is potential participants are restricted to those with writing skills?

S. I agree with that. Would be interested in how it works out though.

R. So am I, but you'll get updates on that. At the beginning of this process, you were asked if you would give a personal final statement. It is nothing to do with the project as such but gives your reflections on the effect of the therapy. It was voluntary, but I understand you have prepared one. Let's finish with that and then we are invited to join David Stephens, our project director, and the research team for a celebratory drink. I think there is bubbly and nibbles on offer. Are you happy to join us?

S. Of course, would love to. It's been an incredible experience in so many ways and I would love to meet everybody. I'll just read out my statement.

My revelations from the therapy:

Lee and I gave each other many years of love, support and caring friendship. I like to think we held each other in a place of safety. I like to think both our lives were enriched by our marriage, but ultimately it was not enough. I needed to grow, to move onward, and he could not match that. I have come to accept that we were flawed with fault lines running through both of us, compatibly but fatally flawed. I was too shuttered to realise what was happening and to let more light in from outside, to recognise my own failures of perception. We were both proud and reluctant, no, let's be honest, too afraid of facing the truth that the time had come to part. Instead, we followed a painful road to that discovery. We were travelling along divergent trajectories, both, in our own ways, retreating from facing the truth. We became our own worst enemies, leading us to destroy something infinitely precious, our coupledom. All the resulting hurt and sorrow permeated down to the unconscious, dwelling there, waiting for their time; the moment for resurrection and absolution. That has now arrived.

Acknowledgements

I am grateful to Moniack Mhor, Scotland's Creative Writing Centre, for kick starting the idea and for support later in the process. Writing is a lonely occupation as ultimately the writer faces the page alone. I received mentoring help from several people. I thank Helen for getting me over the initial finishing line, Anne for pointing out that the journey is more important than the end and Paula Hall for her workshops on porn and sex addiction. I was very fortunate to have the two 'A's as both supportive friends and critical friends. Together they ensured that the book was not only completed but in a better shape than when it began. My heart felt thanks to all of you. Many thanks to Glenda for the cover artwork and Duncan of Lumphanan Press for his publishing skills, encouragement and expertise.

About the author

During a long and varied life, J. McKay has been in many different jobs and situations including working as a couple counsellor. She thought it about time she had a go at writing, better late than never. Currently more or less retired she enjoys pottering round her garden in Southern Scotland.